Grade 5
Module 6

Eureka Math™
A Story of Units

Special thanks go to the Gordan A. Cain Center and to the Department of
Mathematics at Louisiana State University for their support in the development of
Eureka Math.

Published by Common Core

Copyright © 2014 Common Core, Inc. All rights reserved. No part of this work may be reproduced or used in any form or by any means – graphic, electronic, or mechanical, including photocopying or information storage and retrieval systems – without written permission from the copyright holder. "Common Core" and "Common Core, Inc.," are registered trademarks of Common Core, Inc.

Common Core, Inc. is not affiliated with the Common Core State Standards Initiative.

Printed in the U.S.A.
This book may be purchased from the publisher at greatminds.net
10 9 8 7 6 5 4 3 2

ISBN 978-1-63255-038-5

Name _____   Date _____

1. Each shape was placed at a point on the number line S. Give the coordinate of each point below.

    a.  _____   b. ☆ _____

    c. ● _____   d. ▢ _____

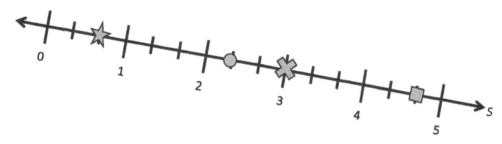

2. Plot the points on the number lines.

a.	b.

Plot A so that its distance from the origin is 2.	Plot R so that its distance from the origin is $\frac{5}{2}$.
c.	d.
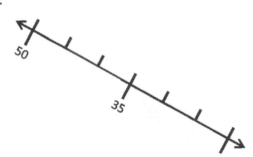	 Plot a point T so that its distance from the origin is $\frac{2}{3}$ more than that of S.
Plot L so that its distance from the origin is 20.	

3. Number line **G** is labeled from 0 to 6. Use number line **G** below to answer the questions.

G

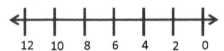

6   5   4   3   2   1   0

a. Plot point A at $\frac{3}{4}$.

b. Label a point that lies at $4\frac{1}{2}$ as B.

c. Label a point, C, whose distance from zero is 5 more than that of A.

The coordinate of C is _____.

d. Plot a point, D, whose distance from zero is $1\frac{1}{4}$ less than that of B.

The coordinate of D is _____.

e. The distance of E from zero is $1\frac{3}{4}$ more than that of D. Plot point E.

f. What is the coordinate of the point that lies halfway between A and D? _____
    Label this point F.

4. Mrs. Fan asked her fifth-grade class to create a number line. Lenox created the number line below:

12   10   8   6   4   2   0

Parks said Lenox's number line is wrong because numbers should always increase from left to right. Who is correct? Explain your thinking.

5. A pirate marked the palm tree on his treasure map and buried his treasure 30 feet away. Do you think he'll be able to easily find his treasure when he returns? Why or why not? What might he do to make it easier to find?

Look for the treasure 30 feet from this tree!

EUREKA MATH™   Lesson 1:   Construct a coordinate system on a line.

2

Name _____   Date _____

1. Answer the following questions using number line Q, below.

    a. What is the coordinate, or the distance from the origin, of the  ? _____

    b. What is the coordinate of ? _____

    c. What is the coordinate of  ? _____

    d. What is the coordinate at the midpoint of and 🩶 ? _____

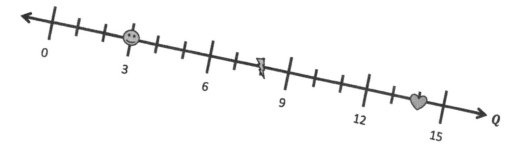

2. Use the number lines to answer the questions.

Plot T so that its distance from the origin is 10.

Plot M so that its distance is $\frac{11}{4}$ from the origin. What is the distance from P to M?

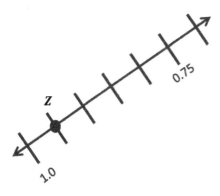

Plot a point that is 0.15 closer to the origin than Z.

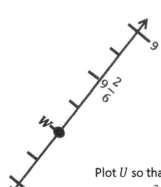

Plot U so that its distance from the origin is $\frac{3}{6}$ less than that of W.

EUREKA MATH™   Lesson 1:   Construct a coordinate system on a line.

3

3. Number line K shows 12 units. Use number line K, below, to answer the questions.

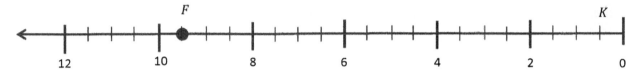

F

K

12   10   8   6   4   2   0

a. Plot a point at 1. Label it A.

b. Label a point that lies at $3\frac{1}{2}$ as B.

c. Label a point, C, whose distance from zero is 8 units farther than that of B.

The coordinate of C is _____.

d. Plot a point, D, whose distance from zero is $\frac{6}{2}$ less than that of B.

The coordinate of D is _____.

e. What is the coordinate of the point that lies $\frac{17}{2}$ farther from the origin than D?

Label this point E.

f. What is the coordinate of the point that lies halfway between F and D?

Label this point G.

4. Mr. Baker's fifth-grade class buried a time capsule in the field behind the school. They drew a map and marked the location of the capsule with an ✖ so that his class can dig it up in ten years. What could Mr. Baker's class have done to make the capsule easier to find?

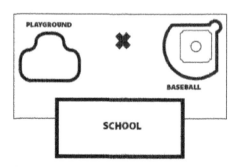

PLAYGROUND

BASEBALL

SCHOOL

Name _____   Date _____

1. a. Use a set square to draw a line perpendicular to the x-axes through points P, Q, and R. Label the new line as the y-axis.

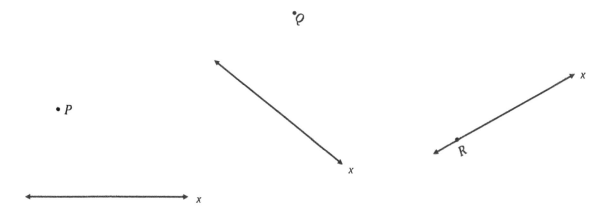

    b. Choose one of the sets of perpendicular lines above and create a coordinate plane. Mark 7 units on each axis and label them as whole numbers.

2. Use the coordinate plane to answer the following.

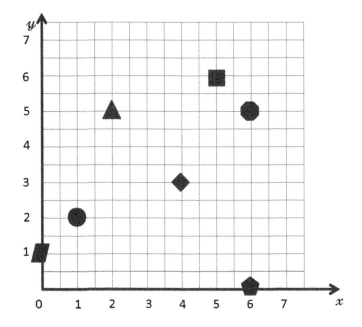

    a. Tell the shape at each location.

x-coordinate	y-coordinate	Shape
2	5	
1	2	
5	6	
6	5	

    b. Which shape is 2 units from the y-axis?

    c. Which shape has an x-coordinate of 0?

    d. Which shape is 4 units from the y-axis and 3 units from the x-axis?

3. Use the coordinate plane to answer the following.

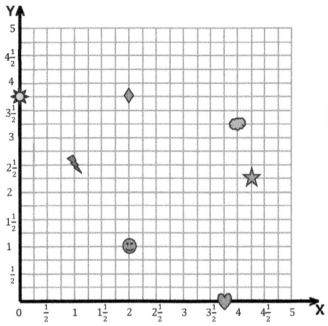

a. Fill in the blanks.

Shape	x-coordinate	y-coordinate
Smiley Face		
Diamond		
Sun		
Heart		

b. Name the shape whose x-coordinate is $\frac{1}{2}$ more than the value of the heart's x-coordinate.

c. Plot a triangle at (3, 4).   d. Plot a square at $(4\frac{3}{4}, 5)$.   e. Plot an X at $(\frac{1}{2}, \frac{3}{4})$.

4. The pirate's treasure is buried at the ✖ on the map.
How could a coordinate plane make describing its
location easier?

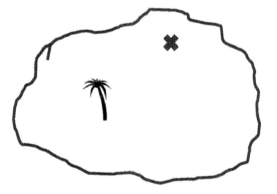

EUREKA MATH   Lesson 2:   Construct a coordinate system on a plane.

6

Name _____   Date _____

1. a. Use a set square to draw a line perpendicular to the x-axis through point P. Label the new line as the y-axis.

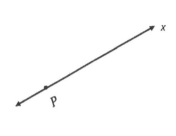

    b. Choose one of the sets of perpendicular lines above and create a coordinate plane. Mark 5 units on each axis, and label them as whole numbers.

2. Use the coordinate plane to answer the following.

    a. Name the shape at each location.

x-coordinate	y-coordinate	Shape
2	4	
5	4	
1	5	
5	1	

    b. Which shape is 2 units from the x-axis?

    c. Which shape has the same x- and y-coordinate?

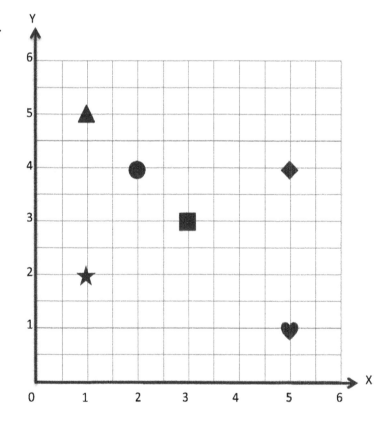

3. Use the coordinate plane to answer the following.

    a. Name the coordinates of each shape.

Shape	x-coordinate	y-coordinate
Moon		
Sun		
Heart		
Cloud		
Smiley Face		

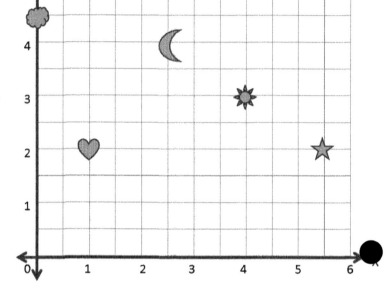

    b. Which 2 shapes have the same y-coordinate?

    c. Plot an X at (2, 3).

    d. Plot a square at $(3, 2\frac{1}{2})$.

    e. Plot a triangle at $(6, 3\frac{1}{2})$.

4. Mr. Palmer plans to bury a time capsule 10 yards behind the school. What else should he do to make naming the location of the time capsule more accurate?

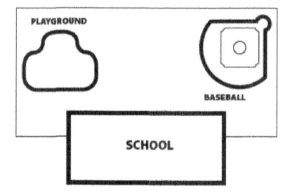

EUREKA MATH™   Lesson 2:   Construct a coordinate system on a plane.

8

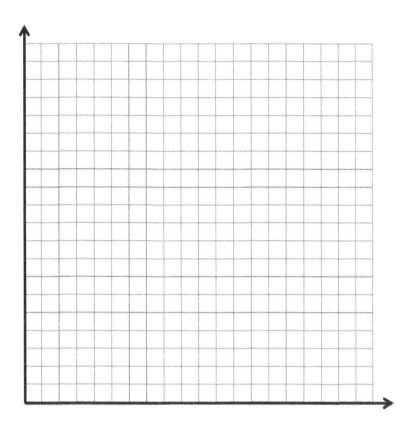

coordinate plane

Name _____   Date _____

1. Use the grid below to complete the following tasks.

    a.   Construct an x-axis that passes through points A and B.

    b.   Construct a perpendicular y-axis that passes through points C and F.

    c.   Label the origin as 0.

    d.   The x-coordinate of B is $5\frac{2}{3}$. Label the whole numbers along the x-axis.

    e.   The y-coordinate of C is $5\frac{1}{3}$. Label the whole numbers along the y-axis.

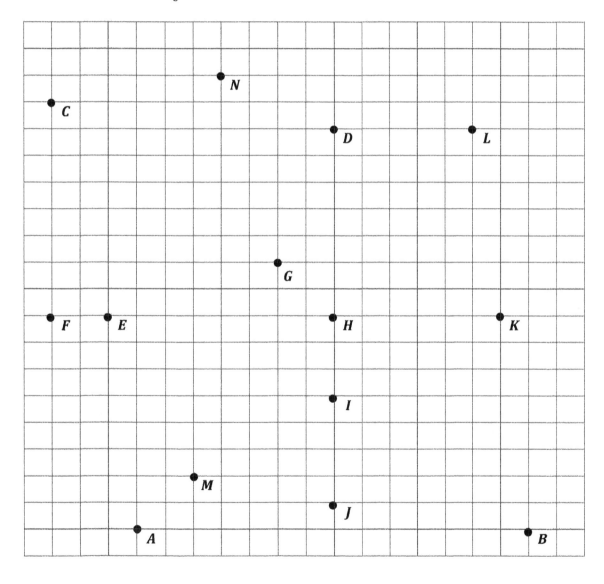

Lesson 3:   Name points using coordinate pairs, and use the coordinate pairs to plot points.

2. For all of the following problems, consider the points A through N on the previous page.

   a. Identify all of the points that have an x-coordinate of $3\frac{1}{3}$.

   b. Identify all of the points that have a y-coordinate of $2\frac{2}{3}$.

   c. Which point is $3\frac{1}{3}$ units above the x-axis **and** $2\frac{2}{3}$ units to the right of the y-axis? Name the point and give its coordinate pair.

   d. Which point is located $5\frac{1}{3}$ units from the y-axis?

   e. Which point is located $1\frac{2}{3}$ units along the x-axis?

   f. Give the coordinate pair for each of the following points.

      $K:$ _____ $I:$ _____ $B:$ _____ $C:$ _____

   g. Name the points located at the following coordinates.

      $(1\frac{2}{3}, \frac{2}{3})$ _____ $(0, 2\frac{2}{3})$ _____ $(1, 0)$ _____ $(2, 5\frac{2}{3})$ _____

   h. Which point has an equal x- and y-coordinate? _____

   i. Give the coordinates for the intersection of the two axes. (____ , ____) Another name for this point on the plane is the _____.

   j. Plot the following points.

      $P: (4\frac{1}{3}, 4)$ $Q: (\frac{1}{3}, 6)$ $R: (4\frac{2}{3}, 1)$ $S: (0, 1\frac{2}{3})$

   k. What is the distance between E and H, or EH?

   l. What is the length of HD?

   m. Would the length of ED be greater or less than $EH + HD$?

   n. Jack was absent when the teacher explained how to describe the location of a point on the coordinate plane. Explain it to him using point J.

Name _____   Date _____

1. Use the grid below to complete the following tasks.

    a. Construct a y-axis that passes through points Y and Z.

    b. Construct a perpendicular x-axis that passes through points Z and X.

    c. Label the origin as 0.

    d. The y-coordinate of W is $2\frac{3}{5}$. Label the whole numbers along the y-axis.

    e. The x-coordinate of V is $2\frac{2}{5}$. Label the whole numbers along the x-axis.

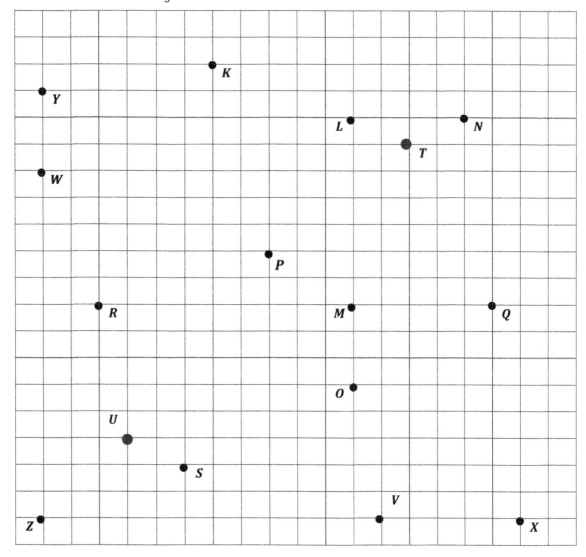

EUREKA MATH | **Lesson 3:** Name points using coordinate pairs, and use the coordinate pairs to plot points.

13

2. For all of the following problems, consider the points K through X on the previous page.

   a. Identify all of the points that have a y-coordinate of $1\frac{3}{5}$.

   b. Identify all of the points that have an x-coordinate of $2\frac{1}{5}$.

   c. Which point is $1\frac{3}{5}$ units above the x-axis *and* $3\frac{1}{5}$ units to the right of the y-axis? Name the point and give its coordinate pair.

   d. Which point is located $1\frac{1}{5}$ units from the y-axis?

   e. Which point is located $\frac{2}{5}$ units along the x-axis?

   f. Give the coordinate pair for each of the following points.
        T: _____ U: _____ S: _____ K: _____

   g. Name the points located at the following coordinates.
        $(\frac{3}{5}, \frac{3}{5})$ _____ $(3\frac{2}{5}, 0)$ _____ $(2\frac{1}{5}, 3)$ _____ $(0, 2\frac{3}{5})$ _____

   h. Plot a point whose x- and y-coordinates are equal. Label your point E.

   i. What is the name for the point on the plane where the two axes intersect? _____ Give the coordinates for this point. (____ , ____)

   j. Plot the following points.

        A: $(1\frac{1}{5}, 1)$ B: $(\frac{1}{5}, 3)$ C: $(2\frac{4}{5}, 2\frac{2}{5})$ D: $(1\frac{1}{5}, 0)$

   k. What is the distance between L and N, or LN?

   l. What is the distance of MQ?

   m. Would RM be greater than, less than, or equal to $LN + MQ$?

   n. Leslie was explaining how to plot points on the coordinate plane to a new student, but she left off some important information. Correct her explanation so that it is complete.

   "All you have to do is read the coordinates; for example, if it says (4, 7), count four, then seven, and put a point where the two grid lines intersect."

EUREKA
MATH™ | Lesson 3:   Name points using coordinate pairs, and use the coordinate pairs to
                             plot points.

14

a.

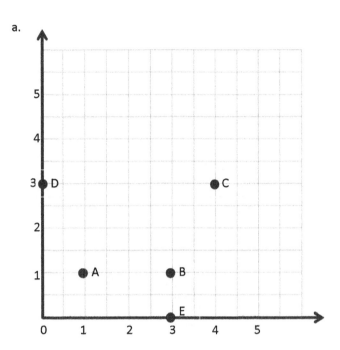

b.

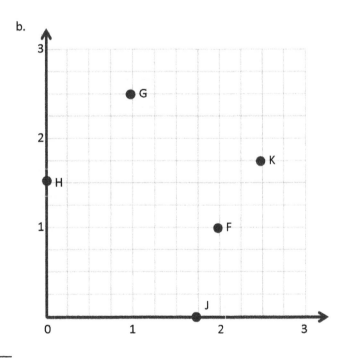

coordinate grid

Lesson 3:   Name points using coordinate pairs, and use the coordinate pairs to
plot points.

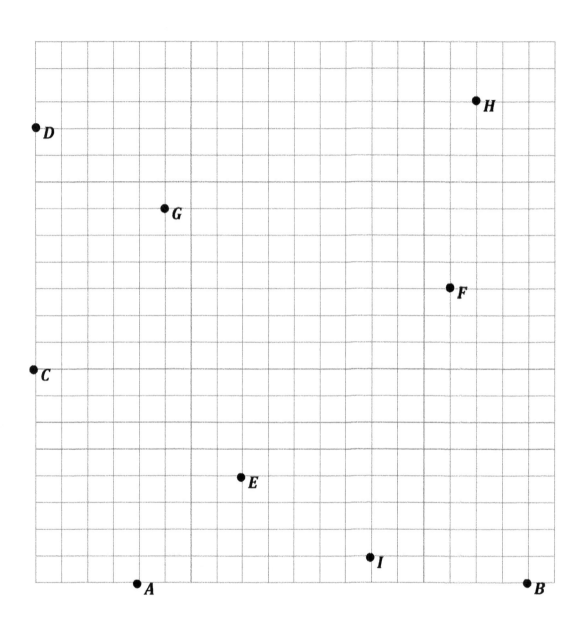

unlabeled coordinate plane

Lesson 3:   Name points using coordinate pairs, and use the coordinate pairs to plot points.

16

Battleship Rules

Goal: To sink all of your opponent's ships by correctly guessing their coordinates.

Materials
- 1 grid sheet (per person/per game)
- Red crayon/marker for hits
- Black crayon/marker for misses
- Folder to place between players

Ships
- Each player must mark 5 ships on the grid.
  - Aircraft Carrier – Plot 5 points
  - Battleship – Plot 4 points
  - Cruiser – Plot 3 points
  - Submarine – Plot 3 points
  - Patrol Boat – Plot 2 points

Setup
- With your opponent, choose a unit length and fractional unit for the coordinate plane.
- Label chosen units on both grid sheets.
- Secretly select locations for each of the 5 ships on your My Ships grid.
  - All ships must be placed horizontally or vertically on the coordinate plane.
  - Ships can touch each other, but they may not occupy the same coordinate.

Play
- Players take turns firing one shot to attack enemy ships.
- On your turn, call out the coordinates of your attacking shot. Record the coordinates of each attack shot.
- Your opponent checks his My Ships grid. If that coordinate is unoccupied, he says, "Miss." If you named a coordinate occupied by a ship, he says, "Hit."
- Mark each attempted shot on your Enemy Ships grid. Mark a black ✖ on the coordinate if your opponent says, "Miss." Mark a red ✓ on the coordinate if your opponent says, "Hit."
- On your opponent's turn, if he hits one of your ships, mark a red ✓ on that coordinate of your My Ships grid. When one of your ships has every coordinate marked with a ✓, say, "You've sunk my [name of ship]."

Victory
- The first player to sink all (or the most) opposing ships, wins.

Lesson 4:   Name points using coordinate pairs, and use the coordinate pairs to plot points.

17

My Ships

- Draw a red ✓ over any coordinate your opponent hits.
- Once all of the coordinates of any ship have been hit, say, "You've sunk my [name of ship]."

aircraft carrier – 5 points
battleship – 4 points
cruiser – 3 points
submarine – 3 points
patrol boat – 2 points

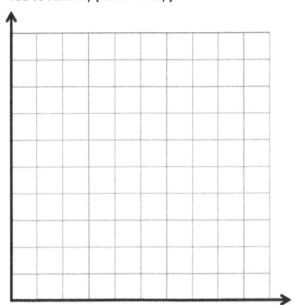

Enemy Ships

- Draw a black ✖ on the coordinate if your opponent says, "Miss."
- Draw a red ✓ on the coordinate if your opponent says, "Hit."
- Draw a circle around the coordinates of a sunken ship.

Attack Shots

- Record the coordinates of each shot below and whether it was a ✓ (hit) or a ✖ (miss).

(_____ , _____)   (_____ , _____)

(_____ , _____)   (_____ , _____)

(_____ , _____)   (_____ , _____)

(_____ , _____)   (_____ , _____)

(_____ , _____)   (_____ , _____)

(_____ , _____)   (_____ , _____)

(_____ , _____)   (_____ , _____)

(_____ , _____)   (_____ , _____)

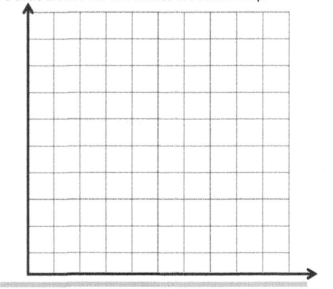

Lesson 4: Name points using coordinate pairs, and use the coordinate pairs to plot points.

Name _____ Date _____

Your homework is to play at least one game of *Battleship* with a friend or family member. You can use the directions from class to teach your opponent. You and your opponent should record your guesses, hits, and misses on the sheet as you did in class.

When you have finished your game, answer these questions.

1. When you guess a point that is a hit, how do you decide which points to guess next?

2. How could you change the coordinate plane to make the game easier or more challenging?

3. Which strategies worked best for you when playing this game?

Lesson 4:   Name points using coordinate pairs, and use the coordinate pairs to plot points.

19

a.
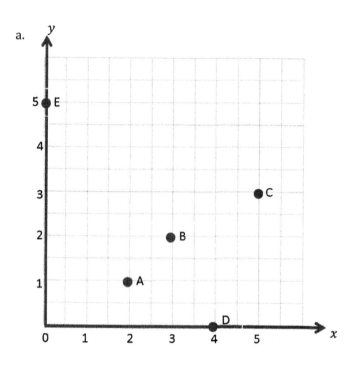

b.
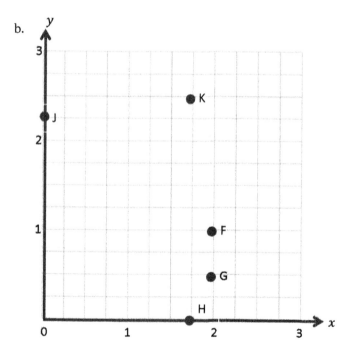

coordinate grid

 | Lesson 4:   Name points using coordinate pairs, and use the coordinate pairs to plot points.

20

Name _____   Date _____

1. Use the coordinate plane to the right to answer the
    following questions.

    a. Use a straightedge to construct a line that goes
        through points A and B. Label the line e.

    b. Line e is parallel to the _____-axis and is
        perpendicular to the _____-axis.

    c. Plot two more points on line e. Name them C and
        D.

    d. Give the coordinates of each point below.

        A: _____ B: _____

        C: _____ D: _____

    e. What do all of the points of line e have in common?

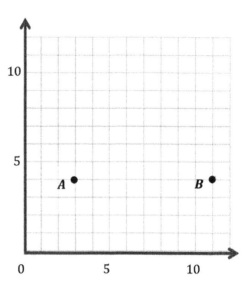

    f. Give the coordinates of another point that would fall on line e with an x-coordinate greater than 15.

2. Plot the following points on the coordinate plane
    to the right.

    P: $(1\frac{1}{2}, \frac{1}{2})$ Q: $(1\frac{1}{2}, 2\frac{1}{2})$

    R: $(1\frac{1}{2}, 1\frac{1}{4})$ S: $(1\frac{1}{2}, \frac{3}{4})$

    a. Use a straightedge to draw a line to connect
        these points. Label the line h.

    b. In line h, $x =$ _____ for all values of y.

    c. Circle the correct word.

        Line h is   *parallel   perpendicular*   to the x-
        axis.

        Line h is   *parallel   perpendicular*   to the y-
        axis.

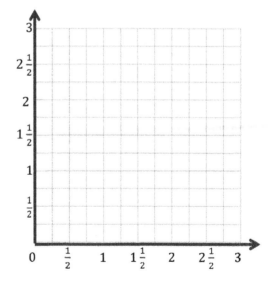

    d. What pattern occurs in the coordinate pairs that let you know that line h is vertical?

EUREKA
MATH™

Lesson 5:   Investigate patterns in vertical and horizontal lines, and interpret
            points on the plane as distances from the axes.

21

3. For each pair of points below, think about the line that joins them. For which pairs is the line parallel to the x-axis? Circle your answer(s). Without plotting them, explain how you know.

   a. (1.4, 2.2) and (4.1, 2.4)   b. (3, 9) and (8, 9)   c. $(1\frac{1}{4}, 2)$ and $(1\frac{1}{4}, 8)$

4. For each pair of points below, think about the line that joins them. For which pairs is the line parallel to the y-axis? Circle your answer(s). Then, give 2 other coordinate pairs that would also fall on this line.

   a. (4, 12) and (6, 12)   b. $(\frac{3}{5}, 2\frac{3}{5})$ and $(\frac{1}{5}, 3\frac{1}{5})$ c. (0.8, 1.9) and (0.8, 2.3)

5. Write the coordinate pairs of 3 points that can be connected to construct a line that is $5\frac{1}{2}$ units to the right of and parallel to the y-axis.

   a. _____   b. _____   c. _____

6. Write the coordinate pairs of 3 points that lie on the x-axis.

   a. _____   b. _____   c. _____

7. Adam and Janice are playing *Battleship*. Presented in the table is a record of Adam's guesses so far.
   He has hit Janice's battleship using these coordinate pairs. What should he guess next? How do you know? Explain, using words and pictures.

(3, 11)	hit
(2, 11)	miss
(3, 10)	hit
(4, 11)	miss
(3, 9)	miss

Name _____   Date _____

1. Use the coordinate plane to answer the questions.
    a. Use a straightedge to construct a line that goes through points A and B. Label the line g.
    b. Line g is parallel to the _____-axis and is perpendicular to the _____-axis.
    c. Draw two more points on line g. Name them C and D.
    d. Give the coordinates of each point below.

        A: _____   B: _____

        C: _____   D: _____

    e. What do all of the points on line g have in common?

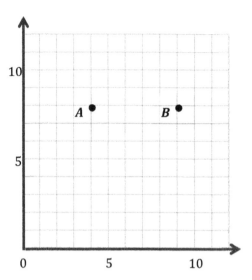

    f. Give the coordinates of another point that falls on line g with an x-coordinate greater than 25.

2. Plot the following points on the coordinate plane to the right.

    $H: (\frac{3}{4}, 3)$ $I: (\frac{3}{4}, 2\frac{1}{4})$

    $J: (\frac{3}{4}, \frac{1}{2})$ $K: (\frac{3}{4}, 1\frac{3}{4})$

    a. Use a straightedge to draw a line to connect these points. Label the line f.

    b. In line f, $x =$ _____ for all values of y.

    c. Circle the correct word:

        Line f is *parallel*   *perpendicular* to the x-axis.

        Line f is *parallel*   *perpendicular* to the y-axis.

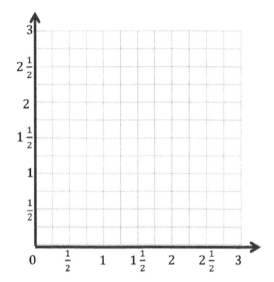

    d. What pattern occurs in the coordinate pairs that make line f vertical?

EUREKA MATH™ | Lesson 5:   Investigate patterns in vertical and horizontal lines, and interpret points on the plane as distances from the axes.

23

3. For each pair of points below, think about the line that joins them. For which pairs is the line parallel to the x-axis? Circle your answer(s). Without plotting them, explain how you know.

    a. (3.2, 7) and (5, 7)   b. (8, 8.4) and (8, 8.8)   c. $(6\frac{1}{2}, 12)$ and (6.2, 11)

4. For each pair of points below, think about the line that joins them. For which pairs is the line parallel to the y-axis? Circle your answer(s). Then, give 2 other coordinate pairs that would also fall on this line.

    a. (3.2, 8.5) and (3.22, 24)   b. $(13\frac{1}{3}, 4\frac{2}{3})$ and $(13\frac{1}{3}, 7)$ c. (2.9, 5.4) and (7.2, 5.4)

5. Write the coordinate pairs of 3 points that can be connected to construct a line that is $5\frac{1}{2}$ units to the right of and parallel to the y-axis.

    a. _____   b. _____   c. _____

6. Write the coordinate pairs of 3 points that lie on the y-axis.

    a. _____   b. _____   c. _____

7. Leslie and Peggy are playing *Battleship* on axes labeled in halves. Presented in the table is a record of Peggy's guesses so far. What should she guess next? How do you know? Explain using words and pictures.

(5, 5)	miss
(4, 5)	hit
$(3\frac{1}{2}, 5)$	miss
$(4\frac{1}{2}, 5)$	miss

EUREKA MATH | Lesson 5:   Investigate patterns in vertical and horizontal lines, and interpret points on the plane as distances from the axes.

24

Point	x	y	(x, y)
H			
I			
J			
K			
L			

a.

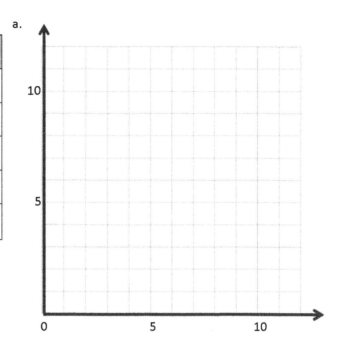

b.

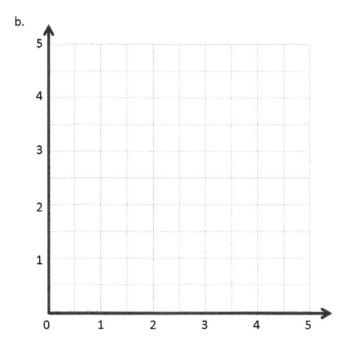

Point	x	y	(x, y)
D	$2\frac{1}{2}$	0	$(2\frac{1}{2}, 0)$
E	$2\frac{1}{2}$	2	$(2\frac{1}{2}, 2)$
F	$2\frac{1}{2}$	4	$(2\frac{1}{2}, 4)$

coordinate plane practice

Lesson 5:   Investigate patterns in vertical and horizontal lines, and interpret
             points on the plane as distances from the axes.

25

Name _____   Date _____

1. Plot the following points, and label them on the coordinate plane.

   A: (0.3, 0.1)   B: (0.3, 0.7)

   C: (0.2, 0.9)   D: (0.4, 0.9)

   a. Use a straightedge to construct line segments
      $\overline{AB}$ and $\overline{CD}$.

   b. Line segment _____ is parallel to the x-axis
      and is perpendicular to the y-axis.

   c. Line segment _____ is parallel to the y-axis
      and is perpendicular to the x-axis.

   d. Plot a point on line segment $\overline{AB}$ that is not at
      the endpoints, and name it U.
      Write the coordinates. U (_____ , _____)

   e. Plot a point on line segment $\overline{CD}$ and name it V. Write the coordinates. V (_____ , _____)

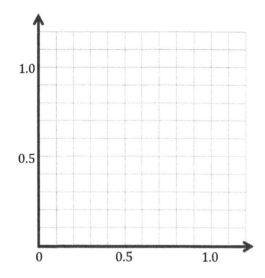

2. Construct line f such that the y-coordinate of every point is $3\frac{1}{2}$, and construct line g such that the
   x-coordinate of every point is $4\frac{1}{2}$.

   a. Line f is _____ units from the x-axis.

   b. Give the coordinates of the point on line f that
      is $\frac{1}{2}$ unit from the y-axis. _____

   c. With a blue pencil, shade the portion of the
      grid that is less than $3\frac{1}{2}$ units from the x-axis.

   d. Line g is _____ units from the y-axis.

   e. Give the coordinates of the point on line g
      that is 5 units from the x-axis. _____

   f. With a red pencil, shade the portion of the grid
      that is more than $4\frac{1}{2}$ units from the y-axis.

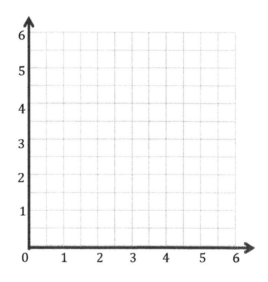

EUREKA
MATH™

Lesson 6:   Investigate patterns in vertical and horizontal lines, and interpret
             points on the plane as distances from the axes.

27

3. Complete the following tasks on the plane below.

   a. Construct a line m that is perpendicular to the x-axis and 3.2 units from the y-axis.

   b. Construct a line a that is 0.8 units from the x-axis.

   c. Construct a line t that is parallel to line m and is halfway between line m and the y-axis.

   d. Construct a line h that is perpendicular to line t and passes through the point (1.2, 2.4).

   e. Using a blue pencil, shade the region that contains points that are more than 1.6 units and less than 3.2 units from the y-axis.

   f. Using a red pencil, shade the region that contains points that are more than 0.8 units and less than 2.4 units from the x-axis.

   g. Give the coordinates of a point that lies in the double-shaded region.

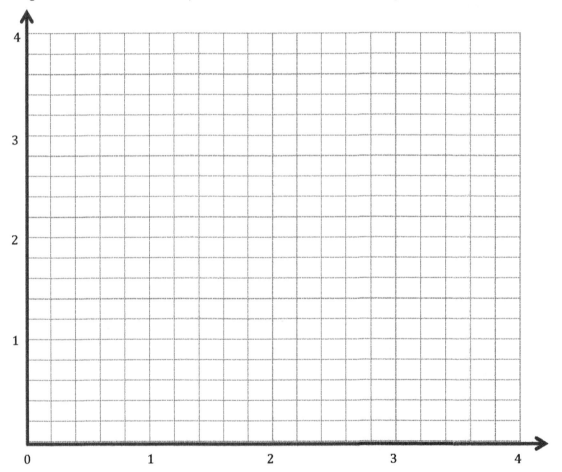

Lesson 6:   Investigate patterns in vertical and horizontal lines, and interpret
points on the plane as distances from the axes.

28

Name _____   Date _____

1. Plot and label the following points on the coordinate plane.

    C: (0.4, 0.4) A: (1.1, 0.4) S: (0.9, 0.5) T: (0.9, 1.1)

    a. Use a straightedge to construct line segments $\overline{CA}$ and $\overline{ST}$.

    b. Name the line segment that is perpendicular to the x-axis and parallel to the y-axis. _____

    c. Name the line segment that is parallel to the x-axis and perpendicular to the y-axis.

        _____

    d. Plot a point on $\overline{CA}$ and name it E. Plot a point on line segment $\overline{ST}$ and name it R.

    e. Write the coordinates of points E and R.

        E (____ , ____) R (____ , ____)

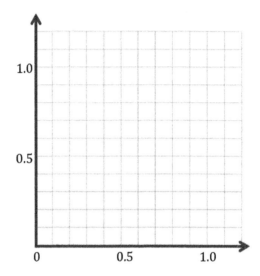

2. Construct line m such that the y-coordinate of every point is $1\frac{1}{2}$, and construct line n such that the x-coordinate of every point is $5\frac{1}{2}$.

    a. Line m is _____ units from the x-axis.

    b. Give the coordinates of the point on line m that is 2 units from the y-axis. _____

    c. With a blue pencil, shade the portion of the grid that is less than $1\frac{1}{2}$ units from the x-axis.

    d. Line n is _____ units from the y-axis.

    e. Give the coordinates of the point on line n that is $3\frac{1}{2}$ units from the x-axis.

    f. With a red pencil, shade the portion of the grid that is less than $5\frac{1}{2}$ units from the y-axis.

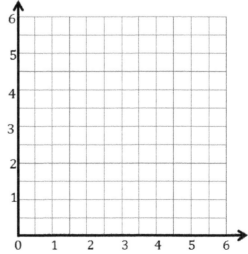

EUREKA MATH™   Lesson 6:   Investigate patterns in vertical and horizontal lines, and interpret
                                   points on the plane as distances from the axes.

                                                                                                    29

3. Construct and label lines e, r, s, o on the plane below.

   a. Line e is 3.75 units above the x-axis.

   b. Line r is 2.5 units from the y-axis.

   c. Line s is parallel to line e but 0.75 farther from the x-axis.

   d. Line o is perpendicular to lines s and e and passes through the point $(3\frac{1}{4}, 3\frac{1}{4})$.

4. Complete the following tasks on the plane.

   a. Using a blue pencil, shade the region that contains points that are more than $2\frac{1}{2}$ units and less than $3\frac{1}{4}$ units from the y-axis.

   b. Using a red pencil, shade the region that contains points that are more than $3\frac{3}{4}$ units and less than $4\frac{1}{2}$ units from the x-axis.

   c. Plot a point that lies in the double shaded region, and label its coordinates.

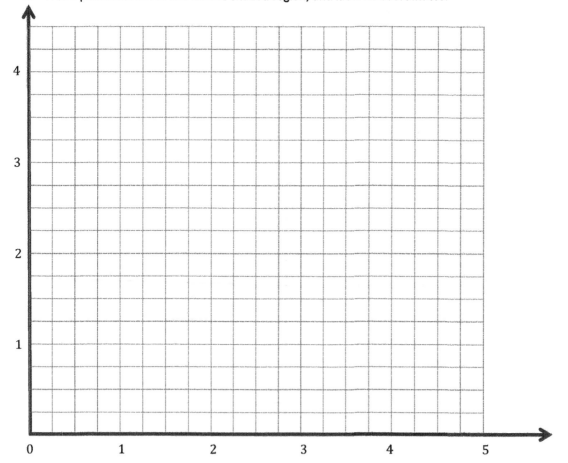

Lesson 6:   Investigate patterns in vertical and horizontal lines, and interpret
             points on the plane as distances from the axes.

30

1,000,000	100,000	10,000	1,000	100	10	1	•	$\frac{1}{10}$	$\frac{1}{100}$	$\frac{1}{1000}$
Millions	Hundred Thousands	Ten Thousands	Thousands	Hundreds	Tens	Ones	•	Tenths	Hundredths	Thousandths
							•			
							•			
							•			
							•			
							•			
							•			
							•			
							•			
							•			

millions through thousandths place value chart

Lesson 6: Investigate patterns in vertical and horizontal lines, and interpret points on the plane as distances from the axes.

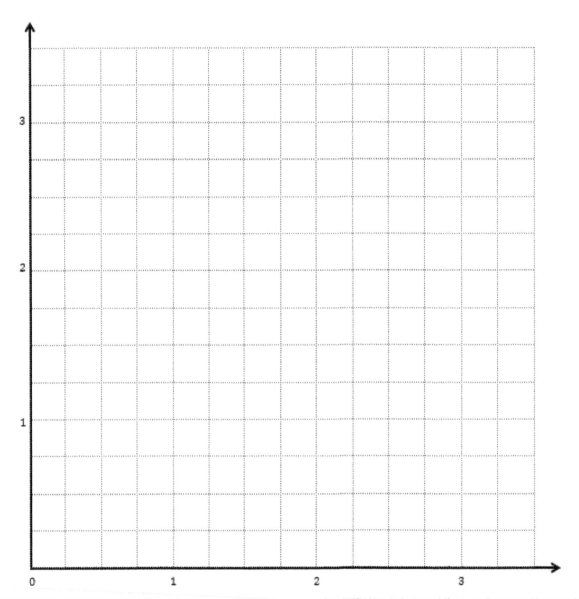

Point	x	y	(x, y)
A			
B			
C			

Point	x	y	(x, y)
D			
E			
F			

coordinate plane

Lesson 6:   Investigate patterns in vertical and horizontal lines, and interpret
points on the plane as distances from the axes.

32

Name _____   Date _____

1. Complete the chart. Then, plot the points on the coordinate plane below.

x	y	(x, y)
0	1	(0, 1)
2	3	
4	5	
6	7	

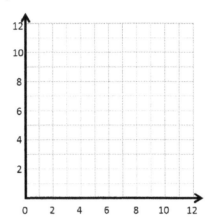

a. Use a straightedge to draw a line connecting these points.

b. Write a rule showing the relationship between the x- and y-coordinates of points on the line.

c. Name 2 other points that are on this line.

_____   _____

2. Complete the chart. Then, plot the points on the coordinate plane below.

x	y	(x, y)
$\frac{1}{2}$	1	
1	2	
$1\frac{1}{2}$	3	
2	4	

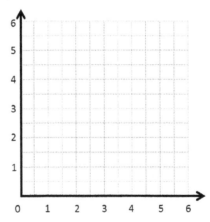

a. Use a straightedge to draw a line connecting these points.

b. Write a rule showing the relationship between the x- and y-coordinates.

c. Name 2 other points that are on this line.   _____   _____

EUREKA MATH™ | Lesson 7:   Plot points, use them to draw lines in the plane, and describe patterns
                                       within the coordinate pairs.

                                                                                                    33

3. Use the coordinate plane below to answer the following questions.

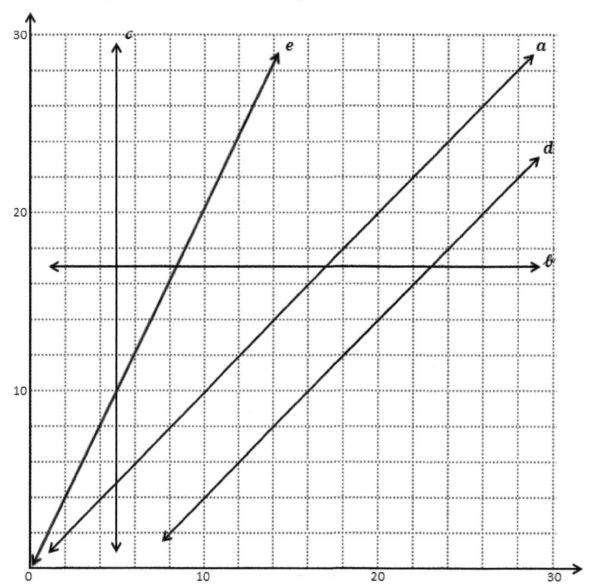

a. Give the coordinates for 3 points that are on line **a**. _____   _____   _____

b. Write a rule that describes the relationship between the x- and y-coordinates for the points on line **a**.

EUREKA MATH   Lesson 7:   Plot points, use them to draw lines in the plane, and describe patterns
                                    within the coordinate pairs.

                                                                                                  34

c. What do you notice about the y-coordinates of every point on line b?

d. Fill in the missing coordinates for points on line d.

     (12, _____)   (6, _____)   (_____, 24)   (36, _____)   (_____, 30)

e. For any point on line c, the x-coordinate is _____.

f. Each of the points lies on at least 1 of the lines shown in the plane above. Identify a line that contains each of the following points.

     i.   (7, 7) ___*a*___   ii.   (14, 8) _____   iii.   (5, 10) _____

     iv.   (0, 17) _____   v.   (15.3, 9.3) _____   vi.   (20, 40) _____

Name _____   Date _____

1. Complete the chart. Then, plot the points on the coordinate plane.

x	y	(x,y)
2	0	
$3\frac{1}{2}$	$1\frac{1}{2}$	
$4\frac{1}{2}$	$2\frac{1}{2}$	
6	4	

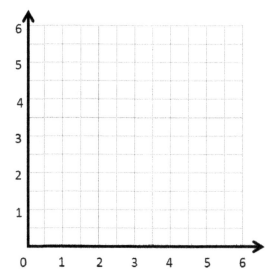

a. Use a straightedge to draw a line connecting these points.

b. Write a rule showing the relationship between the x- and y-coordinates of points on this line.

c. Name two other points that are also on this line.   _____   _____

2. Complete the chart. Then, plot the points on the coordinate plane.

x	y	(x, y)
0	0	
$\frac{1}{4}$	$\frac{3}{4}$	
$\frac{1}{2}$	$1\frac{1}{2}$	
1	3	

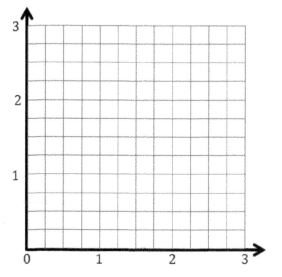

a. Use a straightedge to draw a line connecting these points.

b. Write a rule showing the relationship between the x- and y- coordinates for points on the line.

c. Name two other points that are also on this line.   _____   _____

EUREKA
MATH™

Lesson 7:   Plot points, use them to draw lines in the plane, and describe patterns
             within the coordinate pairs.

36

3. Use the coordinate plane to answer the following questions.

    a. For any point on line m, the x-coordinate is

       _____.

    b. Give the coordinates for 3 points that are on line n.

    c. Write a rule that describes the relationship between the x- and y-coordinates on line n.

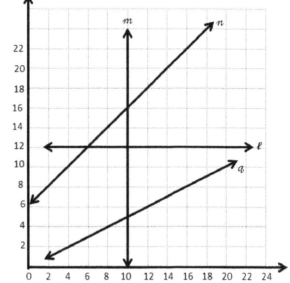

    d. Give the coordinates for 3 points that are on line q.

    e. Write a rule that describes the relationship between the x- and y-coordinates on line q.

    f. Identify a line on which each of these points lie.

       i. (10, 3.2) _____   ii. (12.4, 18.4) _____   iii. (6.45, 12) _____   iv. (14, 7) _____

EUREKA MATH™

Lesson 7: Plot points, use them to draw lines in the plane, and describe patterns within the coordinate pairs.

37

a.

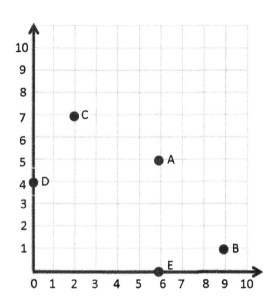

b.

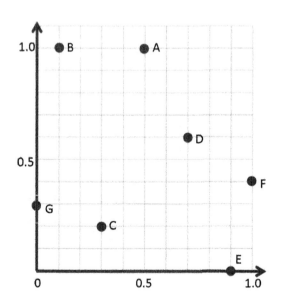

coordinate grid

Lesson 7:   Plot points, use them to draw lines in the plane, and describe patterns within the coordinate pairs.

Name _____   Date _____

1.

a.

Point	x	y	(x, y)
A	0	0	(0, 0)
B	1	1	(1, 1)
C	2	2	(2, 2)
D	3	3	(3, 3)

b.

Point	x	y	(x, y)
G	0	3	(0, 3)
H	$\frac{1}{2}$	$3\frac{1}{2}$	$(\frac{1}{2}, 3\frac{1}{2})$
I	1	4	(1, 4)
J	$1\frac{1}{2}$	$4\frac{1}{2}$	$(1\frac{1}{2}, 4\frac{1}{2})$

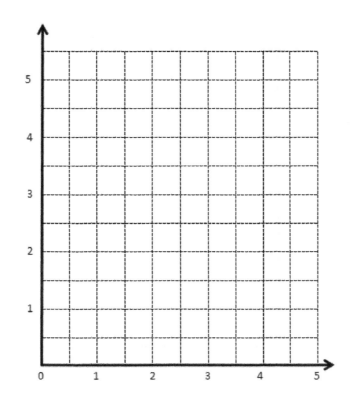

coordinate plane

Lesson 7:   Plot points, use them to draw lines in the plane, and describe patterns within the coordinate pairs.

2.

a.

Point	(x, y)
L	(0, 3)
M	(2, 3)
N	(4, 3)

b.

Point	(x, y)
O	(0, 0)
P	(1, 2)
Q	(2, 4)

c.

Point	(x, y)
R	$(1, \frac{1}{2})$
S	$(2, 1\frac{1}{2})$
T	$(3, 2\frac{1}{2})$

d.

Point	(x, y)
U	(1, 3)
V	(2, 6)
W	(3, 9)

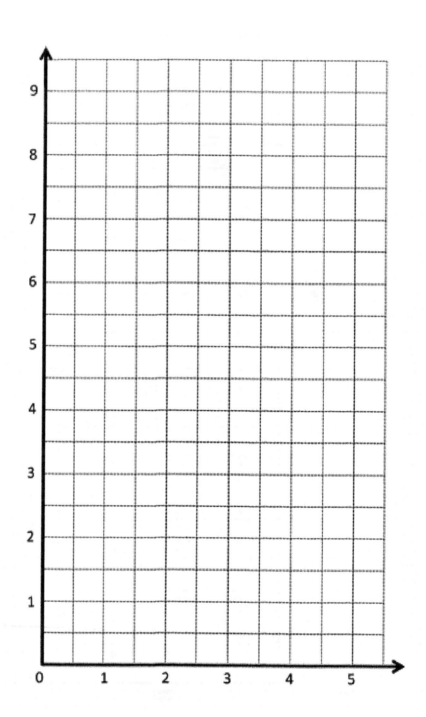

coordinate plane

Lesson 7: Plot points, use them to draw lines in the plane, and describe patterns within the coordinate pairs.

40

Name _____   Date _____

1. Create a table of 3 values for x and y such that each y-coordinate is 3 more than the corresponding x-coordinate.

x	y	(x, y)

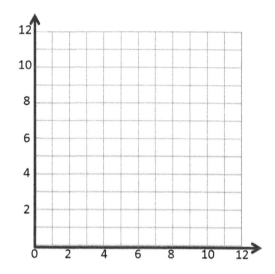

   a. Plot each point on the coordinate plane.

   b. Use a straightedge to draw a line connecting these points.

   c. Give the coordinates of 2 other points that fall on this line with x-coordinates greater than 12.

       (_____ , _____) and (_____ , _____)

2. Create a table of 3 values for x and y such that each y-coordinate is 3 times as much as its corresponding x-coordinate.

x	y	(x, y)

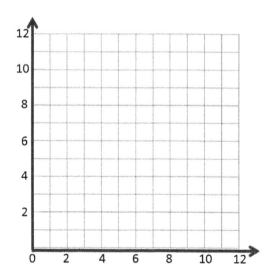

   a. Plot each point on the coordinate plane.

Lesson 8:   Generate a number pattern from a given rule, and plot the points.

41

b. Use a straightedge to draw a line connecting these points.

c. Give the coordinates of 2 other points that fall on this line with y-coordinates greater than 25.

(_____ , _____) and (_____ , _____)

3. Create a table of 5 values for x and y such that each y-coordinate is 1 more than 3 times as much as its corresponding x value.

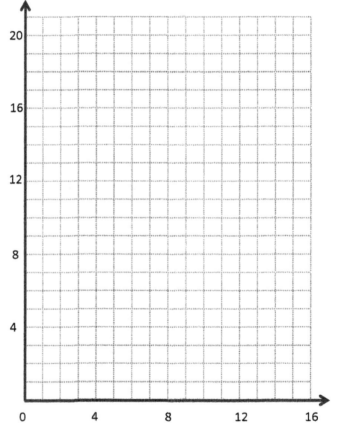

x	y	(x, y)

a. Plot each point on the coordinate plane.

b. Use a straightedge to draw a line connecting these points.

c. Give the coordinates of 2 other points that would fall on this line whose x-coordinates are greater than 12.

(_____ , _____) and (_____ , _____)

Lesson 8:   Generate a number pattern from a given rule, and plot the points.

42

4. Use the coordinate plane below to complete the following tasks.

    a. Graph the lines on the plane.

    line ℓ: x is equal to y

	x	y	(x, y)
A			
B			
C			

    line m: y is 1 more than x

	x	y	(x, y)
G			
H			
I			

    line n: y is 1 more than twice x

	x	y	(x, y)
S			
T			
U			

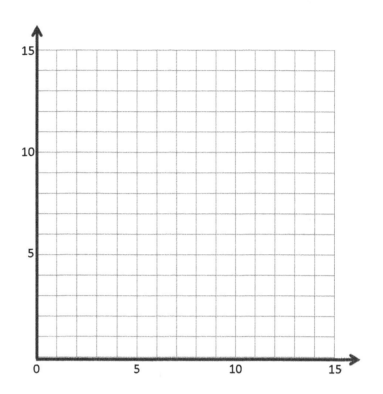

    b. Which two lines intersect? Give the coordinates of their intersection.

    c. Which two lines are parallel?

    d. Give the rule for another line that would be parallel to the lines you listed in (c).

EUREKA
MATH™

Lesson 8:   Generate a number pattern from a given rule, and plot the points.

43

Name _____ Date _____

1. Complete this table such that each y-coordinate is 4 more than the corresponding x-coordinate.

x	y	(x, y)

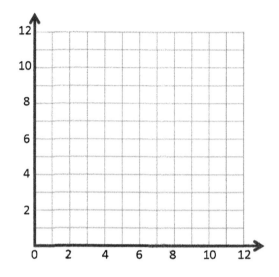

a. Plot each point on the coordinate plane.

b. Use a straightedge to construct a line connecting these points.

c. Give the coordinates of 2 other points that fall on this line with x-coordinates greater than 18.

(_____ , _____) and (_____ , _____)

2. Complete this table such that each y-coordinate is 2 times as much as its corresponding x-coordinate.

x	y	(x, y)

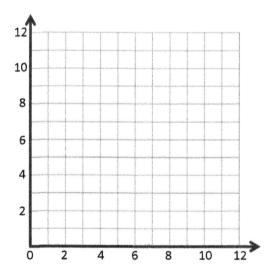

a. Plot each point on the coordinate plane.

b. Use a straightedge to draw a line connecting these points.

c. Give the coordinates of 2 other points that fall on this line with y-coordinates greater than 25.

(_____ , _____) and (_____ , _____)

EUREKA MATH™

Lesson 8: Generate a number pattern from a given rule, and plot the points.

44

3. Use the coordinate plane below to complete the following tasks.

    a. Graph these lines on the plane.

        line ℓ: x is equal to y

	x	y	(x, y)
A			
B			
C			

        line m: y is 1 less than x

	x	y	(x, y)
G			
H			
I			

        line n: y is 1 less than twice x

	x	y	(x, y)
S			
T			
U			

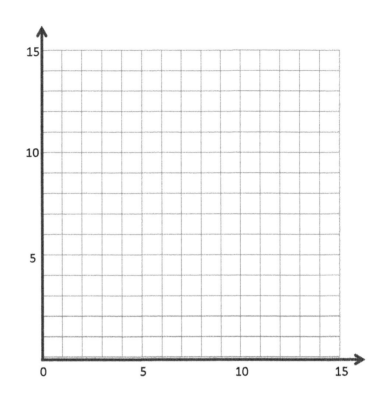

    b. Do any of these lines intersect? If yes, identify which ones, and give the coordinates of their intersection.

    c. Are any of these lines parallel? If yes, identify which ones.

    d. Give the rule for another line that would be parallel to the lines you listed in (c).

EUREKA MATH | Lesson 8:   Generate a number pattern from a given rule, and plot the points.

45

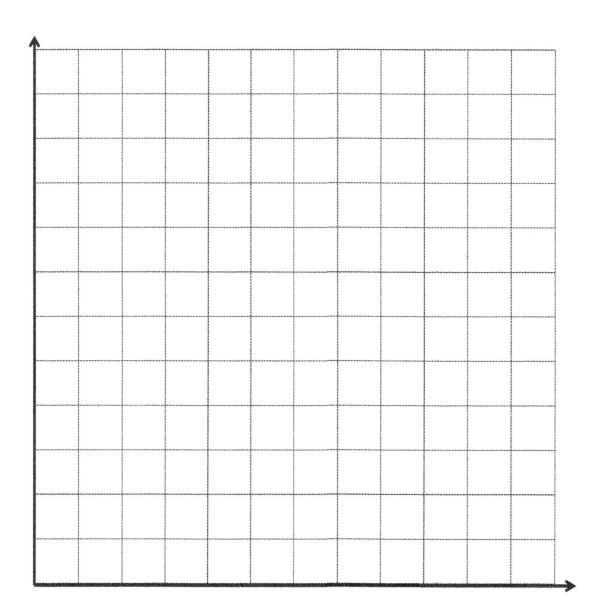

coordinate grid insert

Lesson 8:   Generate a number pattern from a given rule, and plot the points.

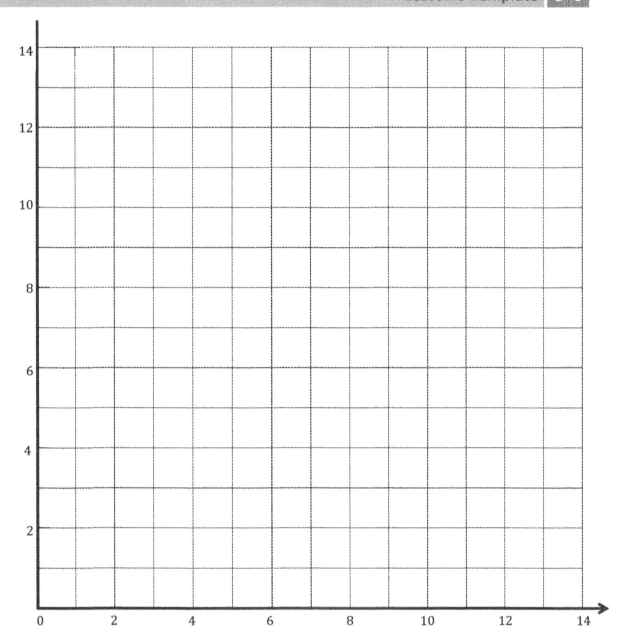

Line *a*:		
x	*y*	(x, y)

Line *b*:		
x	*y*	(x, y)

Line *c*:		
x	*y*	(x, y)

coordinate plane

Lesson 8: Generate a number pattern from a given rule, and plot the points.

47

Name _____   Date _____

1. Complete the table for the given rules.

   Line *a*

   Rule: y is 1 more than x

x	y	(x, y)
1		
5		
9		
13		

   Line *b*

   Rule: y is 4 more than x

x	y	(x, y)
0		
5		
8		
11		

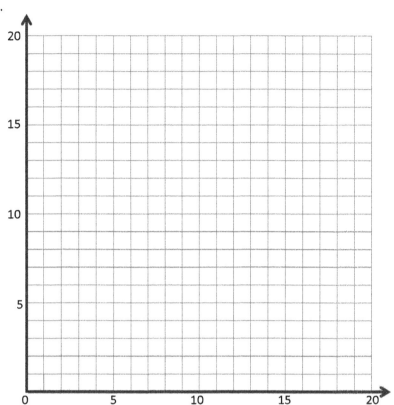

   a. Construct each line on the coordinate plane above.

   b. Compare and contrast these lines.

   c. Based on the patterns you see, predict what line *c*, whose rule is *y is 7 more than x*, would look like. Draw your prediction on the plane above.

EUREKA
MATH™

Lesson 9:   Generate two number patterns from given rules, plot the points, and
             analyze the patterns.

49

2. Complete the table for the given rules.

Line *e*

Rule: y is twice as much as x

x	y	(x, y)
0		
2		
5		
9		

Line *f*

Rule: y is half as much as x

x	y	(x, y)
0		
6		
10		
20		

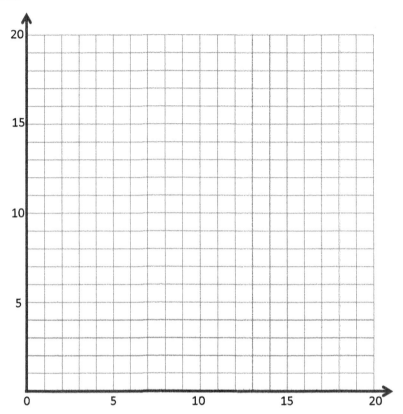

a. Construct each line on the coordinate plane above.

b. Compare and contrast these lines.

c. Based on the patterns you see, predict what line *g*, whose rule is *y is 4 times as much as x*, would look like. Draw your prediction in the plane above.

EUREKA MATH

Lesson 9: Generate two number patterns from given rules, plot the points, and analyze the patterns.

50

Name _____   Date _____

1. Complete the table for the given rules.

    Line **a**

    Rule: y is 1 less than x

x	y	(x, y)
1		
4		
9		
16		

    Line **b**

    Rule: y is 5 less than x

x	y	(x, y)
5		
8		
14		
20		

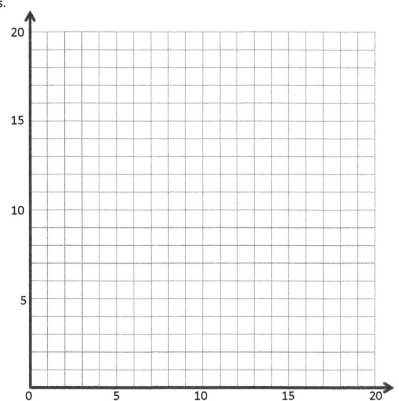

    a. Construct each line on the coordinate plane.

    b. Compare and contrast these lines.

    c. Based on the patterns you see, predict what line **c**, whose rule is *y is 7 less than x*, would look like. Draw your prediction on the plane above.

EUREKA MATH™

Lesson 9: Generate two number patterns from given rules, plot the points, and analyze the patterns.

51

2. Complete the table for the given rules.

Line *e*

Rule: *y is 3 times as much as x*

x	y	(x, y)
0		
1		
4		
6		

Line *f*

Rule: *y is a third as much as x*

x	y	(x, y)
0		
3		
9		
15		

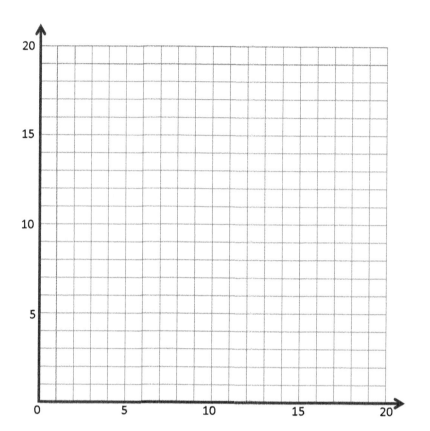

a. Construct each line on the coordinate plane.

b. Compare and contrast these lines.

c. Based on the patterns you see, predict what line *g,* whose rule is *y is 4 times as much as x,* and line *h*, whose rule is *y is one-fourth as much as x*, would look like. Draw your prediction in the plane above.

EUREKA MATH

Lesson 9: Generate two number patterns from given rules, plot the points, and analyze the patterns.

52

Line ℓ   Line *m*

Rule: y is 2 more than x   *Rule:* y is 5 more than x

x	y	(x, y)
1		
5		
10		
15		

x	y	(x, y)
0		
5		
10		
15		

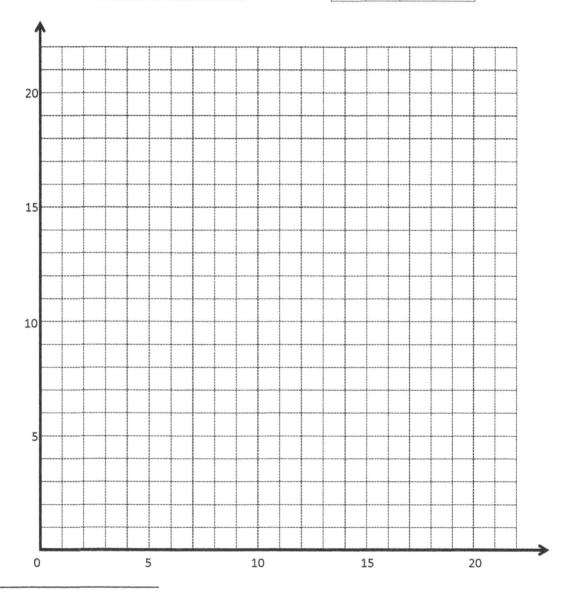

coordinate plane

| **Lesson 9:** | Generate two number patterns from given rules, plot the points, and analyze the patterns. |

Line **p**

Rule: *y is x times 2*

x	y	(x, y)

Line **q**

Rule: *y is x times 3*

x	y	(x, y)

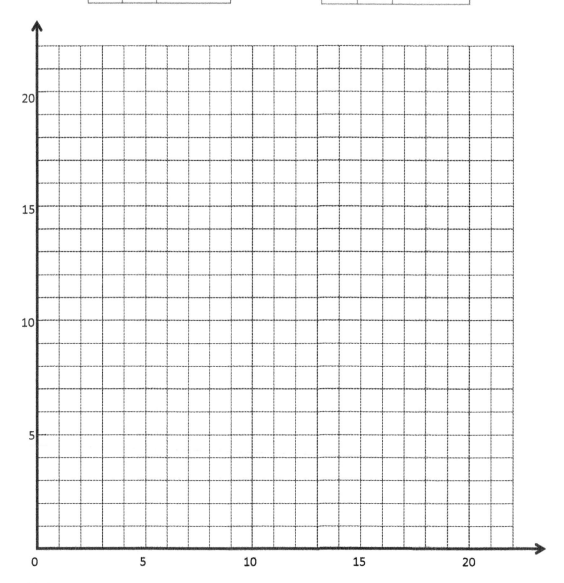

coordinate plane

Lesson 9:   Generate two number patterns from given rules, plot the points, and analyze the patterns.

54

Name _____   Date _____

1. Use the coordinate plane below to complete the following tasks.

    a. Line **p** represents the rule *x and y are equal.*

    b. Construct a line, **d**, that is parallel to line **p** and contains point D.

    c. Name 3 coordinate pairs on line **d**.

    d. Identify a rule to describe line **d**.

    e. Construct a line, **e**, that is parallel to line **p** and contains point E.

    f. Name 3 points on line **e**.

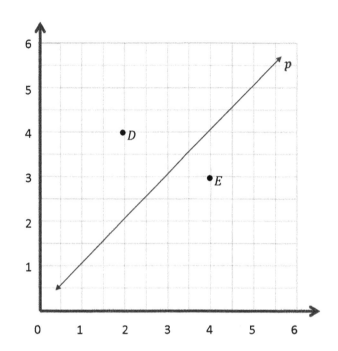

    g. Identify a rule to describe line **e**.

    h. Compare and contrast lines **d** and **e** in terms of their relationship to line **p**.

2. Write a rule for a fourth line that would be parallel to those above and would contain the point $(3\frac{1}{2}, 6)$. Explain how you know.

EUREKA
MATH™ | Lesson 10:   Compare the lines and patterns generated by addition rules and
                                      multiplication rules.

                                                                                              55

3. Use the coordinate plane below to complete the following tasks.

   a. Line **p** represents the rule *x and y are equal.*

   b. Construct a line, **v**, that contains the origin and point V.

   c. Name 3 points on line **v**.

   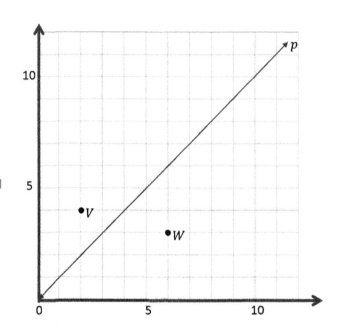

   d. Identify a rule to describe line **v**.

   e. Construct a line, **w**, that contains the origin and point W.

   f. Name 3 points on line **w**.

   g. Identify a rule to describe line **w**.

   h. Compare and contrast lines **v** and **w** in terms of their relationship to line **p**.

   i. What patterns do you see in lines that are generated by multiplication rules?

4. Circle the rules that generate lines that are parallel to each other.

   Add 5 to x   *Multiply x by $\frac{2}{3}$*   *x plus $\frac{1}{2}$*   *x times $1\frac{1}{2}$*

EUREKA
MATH

Lesson 10:   Compare the lines and patterns generated by addition rules and
            multiplication rules.

56

Name _____   Date _____

1. Use the coordinate plane to complete the following tasks.

    a. Line **p** represents the rule *x and y are equal.*

    b. Construct a line, **d**, that is parallel to line **p** and contains point D.

    c. Name 3 coordinate pairs on line **d**.

    d. Identify a rule to describe line **d**.

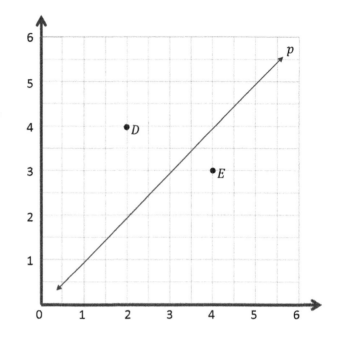

    e. Construct a line, **e**, that is parallel to line **p** and contains point E.

    f. Name 3 points on line **e**.

    g. Identify a rule to describe line **e**.

    h. Compare and contrast lines **d** and **e** in terms of their relationship to line **p**.

EUREKA MATH™ | **Lesson 10:** Compare the lines and patterns generated by addition rules and multiplication rules.

57

2. Write a rule for a fourth line that would be parallel to those above and that would contain the point $(5\frac{1}{2}, 2)$. Explain how you know.

3. Use the coordinate plane below to complete the following tasks.

    a. Line p represents the rule x and y are equal.

    b. Construct a line, v, that contains the origin and point V.

    c. Name 3 points on line v.

    d. Identify a rule to describe line v.

    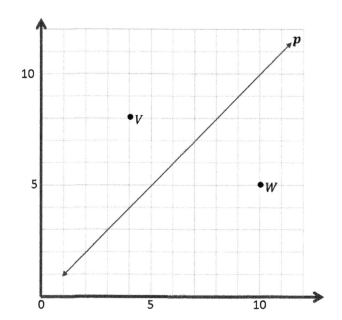

    e. Construct a line, w, that contains the origin and point W.

    f. Name 3 points on line w.

    g. Identify a rule to describe line w.

    h. Compare and contrast lines v and w in terms of their relationship to line p.

    i. What patterns do you see in lines that are generated by multiplication rules?

EUREKA
MATH™ | Lesson 10:   Compare the lines and patterns generated by addition rules and
                            multiplication rules.

                                                                                        58

Line **p**

Line **b**

Line **c**

Line **d**

Rule: *y is 0 more than x*

Rule: _____

Rule: _____

Rule: _____

x	y	(x, y)
0		
5		
10		
15		

x	y	(x, y)
7		
10		
13		
18		

x	y	(x, y)
2		
4		
8		
11		

x	y	(x, y)
5		
7		
12		
15		

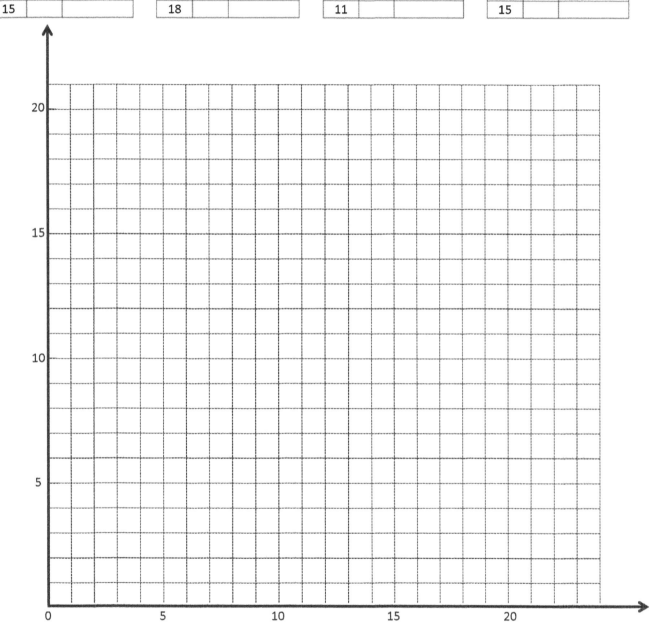

coordinate plane

Lesson 10:   Compare the lines and patterns generated by addition rules and
multiplication rules.

Line **g** Rule: _____

x	y	(x, y)
1		
2		
5		
7		

Line **h** Rule: _____

x	y	(x, y)
3		
6		
12		
15		

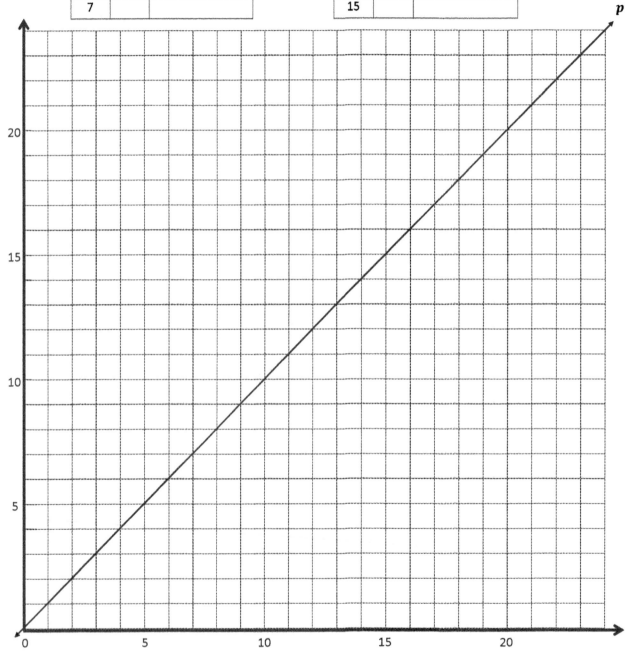

coordinate plane

Lesson 10: Compare the lines and patterns generated by addition rules and multiplication rules.

60

Name _____   Date _____

1. Complete the tables for the given rules.

Line ℓ

Rule: Double x

x	y	(x, y)
0		
1		
2		
3		

Line m

Rule: Double x, then add 1

x	y	(x, y)
0		
1		
2		
3		

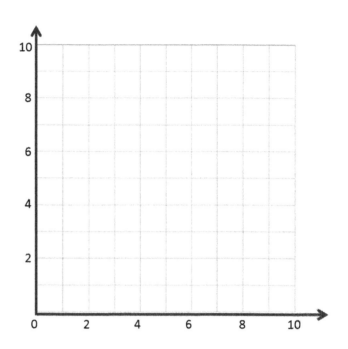

a. Draw each line on the coordinate plane above.

b. Compare and contrast these lines.

c. Based on the patterns you see, predict what the line for the rule *double x, then subtract 1* would look like. Draw the line on the plane above.

2. Circle the point(s) that the line for the rule *multiply x by $\frac{1}{3}$, then add 1* would contain.

$(0, \frac{1}{3})$ $(2, 1\frac{2}{3})$ $(1\frac{1}{2}, 1\frac{1}{2})$ $(2\frac{1}{4}, 2\frac{1}{4})$

a. Explain how you know.

b. Give two other points that fall on this line.

3. Complete the tables for the given rules.

Line ℓ

Rule: Halve x

x	y	(x, y)
0		
1		
2		
3		

Line m

Rule: Halve x, then add $1\frac{1}{2}$

x	y	(x, y)
0		
1		
2		
3		

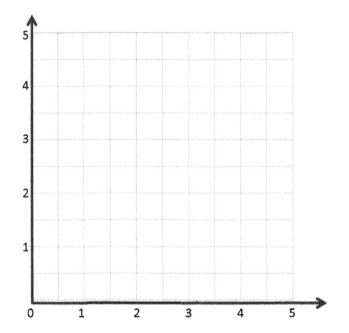

a. Draw each line on the coordinate plane above.

b. Compare and contrast these lines.

c. Based on the patterns you see, predict what the line for the rule *halve x, then subtract 1* would look like. Draw the line on the plane above.

4. Circle the point(s) that the line for the rule *multiply x by $\frac{2}{3}$, then subtract 1* would contain.

$(1\frac{1}{3}, \frac{1}{9})$ $(2, \frac{1}{3})$ $(1\frac{3}{2}, 1\frac{1}{2})$ $(3, 1)$

a. Explain how you know.

b. Give two other points that fall on this line.

EUREKA MATH™   Lesson 11:   Analyze number patterns created from mixed operations.

62

Name _____   Date _____

1. Complete the tables for the given rules.

Line ℓ

Rule: Double x

x	y	(x, y)
1		
2		
3		

Line m

Rule: Double x, then subtract 1

x	y	(x, y)
1		
2		
3		

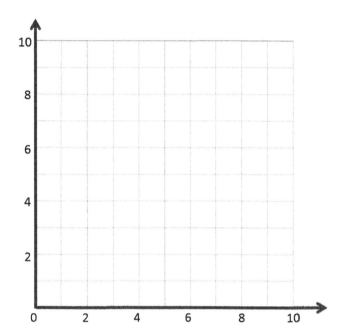

a. Draw each line on the coordinate plane above.

b. Compare and contrast these lines.

c. Based on the patterns you see, predict what the line for the rule *double x, then add 1* would look like. Draw your prediction on the plane above.

2. Circle the point(s) that the line for the rule *multiply x by $\frac{1}{2}$, then add 1* would contain.

$(0, \frac{1}{2})$ $(2, 1\frac{1}{4})$ $(2, 2)$ $(3, \frac{1}{2})$

a. Explain how you know.

b. Give two other points that fall on this line.

3. Complete the tables for the given rules.

Line ℓ

Rule: Halve x, then add 1

x	y	(x, y)
0		
1		
2		
3		

Line m

Rule: Halve x, then add $1\frac{1}{4}$

x	y	(x, y)
0		
1		
2		
3		

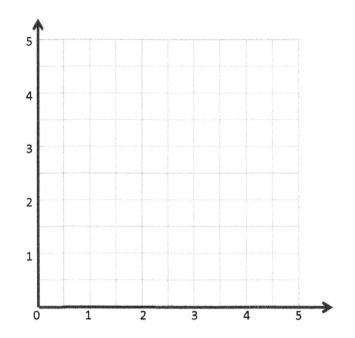

a. Draw each line on the coordinate plane above.

b. Compare and contrast these lines.

c. Based on the patterns you see, predict what the line for the rule *halve x, then subtract 1* would look like. Draw your prediction on the plane above.

4. Circle the point(s) that the line for the rule *multiply x by $\frac{3}{4}$, then subtract $\frac{1}{2}$* would contain.

$(1, \frac{1}{4})$ $(2, \frac{1}{4})$ $(3, 1\frac{3}{4})$ $(3, 1)$

a. Explain how you know.

b. Give two other points that fall on this line.

Line ℓ

Rule: Triple x

x	y	(x, y)
0		
1		
2		
4		

Line m

Rule: Triple x, then add 3

x	y	(x, y)
0		
1		
2		
3		

Line n

Rule: Triple x, then subtract 2

x	y	(x, y)
1		
2		
3		
4		

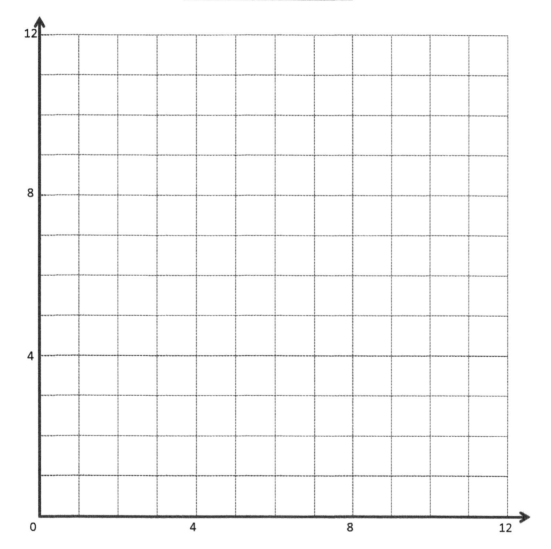

coordinate plane

Lesson 11:   Analyze number patterns created from mixed operations.

Name _____   Date _____

1. Write a rule for the line that contains the points $(0, \frac{3}{4})$ and $(2\frac{1}{2}, 3\frac{1}{4})$.

    a. Identify 2 more points on this line. Draw the line on the grid below.

Point	x	y	(x, y)
B			
C			

    b. Write a rule for a line that is parallel to $\overleftrightarrow{BC}$ and goes through point $(1, \frac{1}{4})$.

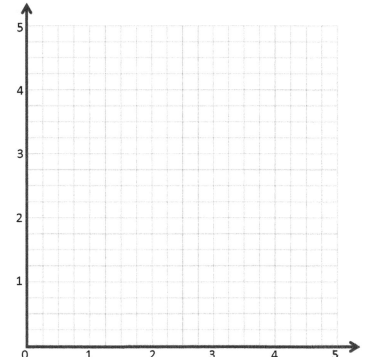

2. Create a rule for the line that contains the points $(1, \frac{1}{4})$ and $(3, \frac{3}{4})$.

    a. Identify 2 more points on this line. Draw the line on the grid at right.

Point	x	y	(x, y)
G			
H			

    b. Write a rule for a line that passes through the origin and lies between $\overleftrightarrow{BC}$ and $\overleftrightarrow{GH}$.

3. Create a rule for a line that contains the point $(\frac{1}{4}, 1\frac{1}{4})$, using the operation or description below. Then, name 2 other points that would fall on each line.

a. Addition: _____

Point	x	y	(x, y)
T			
U			

b. A line parallel to the x-axis: _____

Point	x	y	(x, y)
G			
H			

c. Multiplication: _____

Point	x	y	(x, y)
A			
B			

d. A line parallel to the y-axis: _____

Point	x	y	(x, y)
V			
W			

e. Multiplication with addition: _____

Point	x	y	(x, y)
R			
S			

4. Mrs. Boyd asked her students to give a rule that could describe a line that contains the point (0.6, 1.8). Avi said the rule could be *multiply x by 3*. Ezra claims this could be a vertical line, and the rule could be *x is always 0.6*. Erik thinks the rule could be *add 1.2 to x*. Mrs. Boyd says that all the lines they are describing could describe a line that contains the point she gave. Explain how that is possible, and draw the lines on the coordinate plane to support your response.

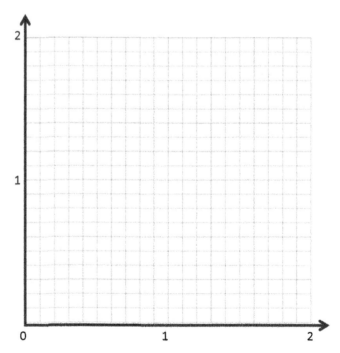

EUREKA MATH™ | **Lesson 12:**   Create a rule to generate a number pattern, and plot the points.

68

Extension:

5. Create a mixed operation rule for the line that contains the points (0, 1) and (1, 3).

a. Identify 2 more points, O and P, on this line. Draw the line on the grid.

Point	x	y	(x, y)
O			
P			

b. Write a rule for a line that is parallel to $\overleftrightarrow{OP}$ and goes through point $(1, 2\frac{1}{2})$.

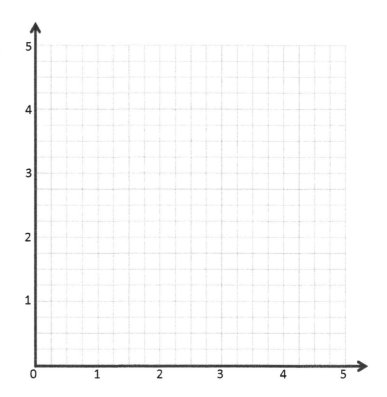

EUREKA MATH   Lesson 12:   Create a rule to generate a number pattern, and plot the points.

69

Name _____   Date _____

1. Write a rule for the line that contains the points $(0, \frac{1}{4})$ and $(2\frac{1}{2}, 2\frac{3}{4})$.

    a. Identify 2 more points on this line. Draw the line on the grid below.

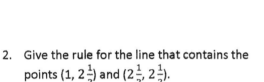

    b. Write a rule for a line that is parallel
        to $\overleftrightarrow{BC}$ and goes through point $(1, 2\frac{1}{4})$.

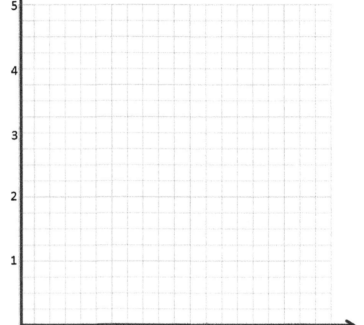

2. Give the rule for the line that contains the
    points $(1, 2\frac{1}{2})$ and $(2\frac{1}{2}, 2\frac{1}{2})$.

    a. Identify 2 more points on this line.
        Draw the line on the grid above.

Point	x	y	(x, y)
G			
H			

    b. Write a rule for a line that is parallel to $\overleftrightarrow{GH}$.

EUREKA MATH™   Lesson 12:   Create a rule to generate a number pattern, and plot the points.

70

3. Give the rule for a line that contains the point ($\frac{3}{4}$, $1\frac{1}{2}$), using the operation or description below. Then, name 2 other points that would fall on each line.

a. Addition: _____

Point	x	y	(x, y)
T			
U			

b. A line parallel to the x-axis: _____

Point	x	y	(x, y)
G			
H			

c. Multiplication: _____

Point	x	y	(x, y)
A			
B			

d. A line parallel to the y-axis: _____

Point	x	y	(x, y)
V			
W			

e. Multiplication with addition: _____

Point	x	y	(x, y)
R			
S			

4. On the grid, two lines intersect at (1.2, 1.2). If line a passes through the origin, and line b contains the point (1.2, 0), write a rule for line a and line b.

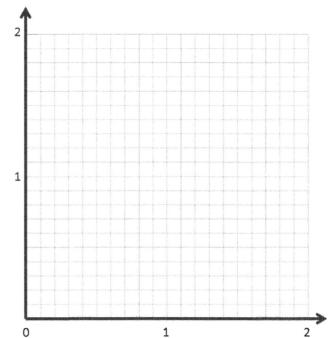

EUREKA MATH™ | Lesson 12:   Create a rule to generate a number pattern, and plot the points.

71

Line l Line m

Rule: _____   Rule: _____

Point	x	y	(x, y)
A	$1\frac{1}{2}$	3	$(1\frac{1}{2}, 3)$
B			
C			
D			

Point	x	y	(x, y)
A			
E			
F			
G			

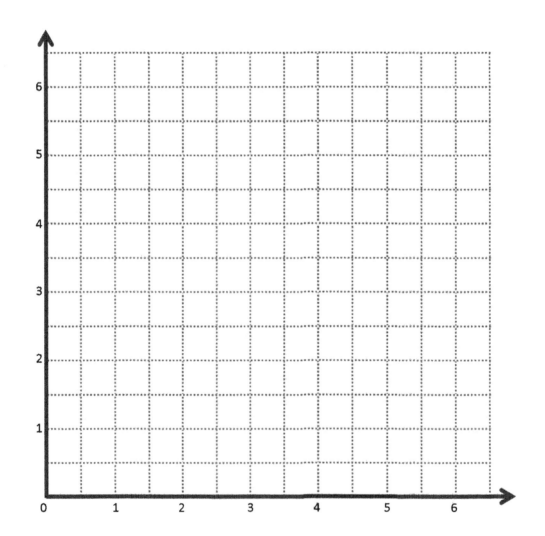

coordinate plane

Lesson 12:   Create a rule to generate a number pattern, and plot the points.

Name _____ Date _____

1. Use a right angle template and straightedge to draw at least four sets of parallel lines in the space below.

2. Circle the segments that are parallel.

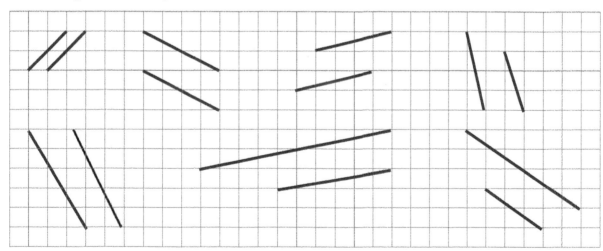

Lesson 13: Construct parallel line segments on a rectangular grid.

73

3. Use your straightedge to draw a segment parallel to each segment through the given point.

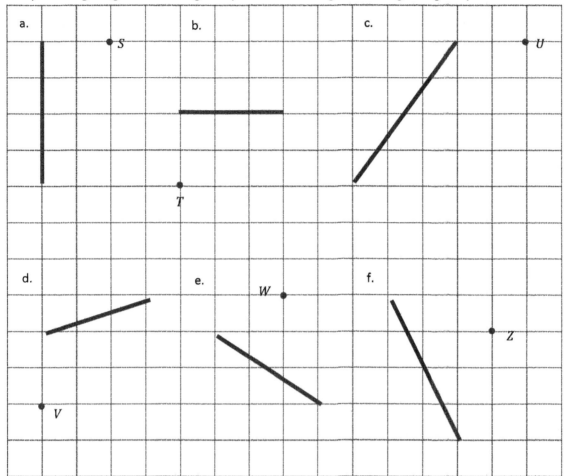

4. Draw 2 different lines parallel to line *b*.

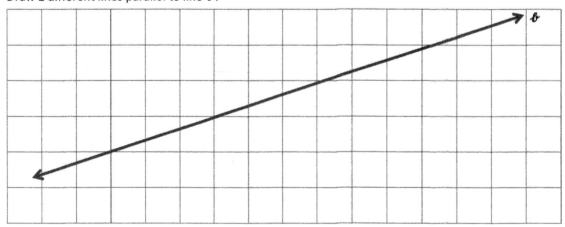

EUREKA MATH

Lesson 13: Construct parallel line segments on a rectangular grid.

74

Name _____ Date _____

1. Use your right angle template and straightedge to draw at least three sets of parallel lines in the space below.

2. Circle the segments that are parallel.

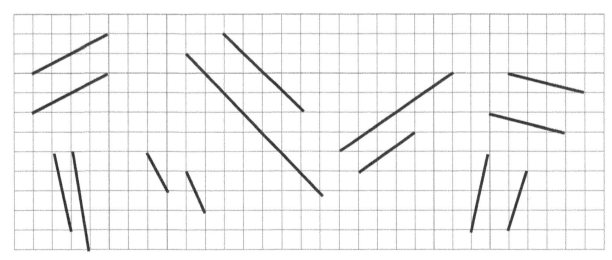

EUREKA
MATH

Lesson 13: Construct parallel line segments on a rectangular grid.

75

3. Use your straightedge to draw a segment parallel to each segment through the given point.

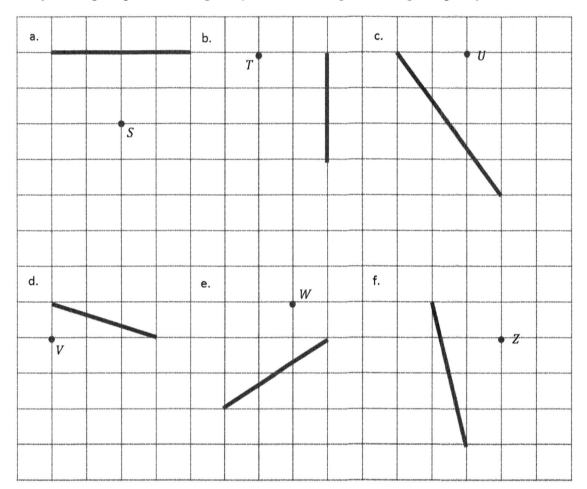

4. Draw 2 different lines parallel to line ℓ.

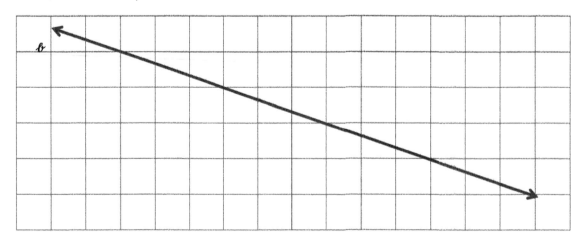

EUREKA MATH   Lesson 13:   Construct parallel line segments on a rectangular grid.

76

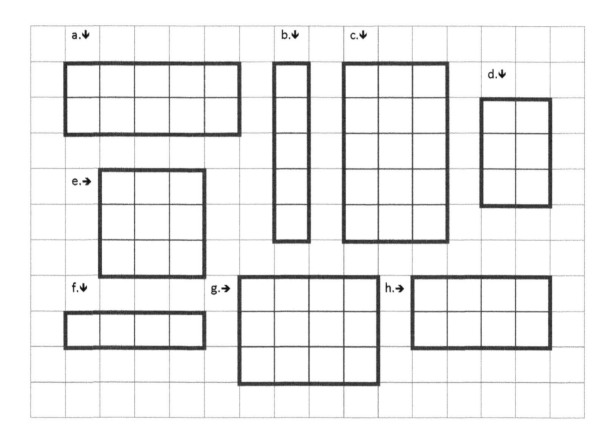

rectangles

Lesson 13:   Construct parallel line segments on a rectangular grid.

77

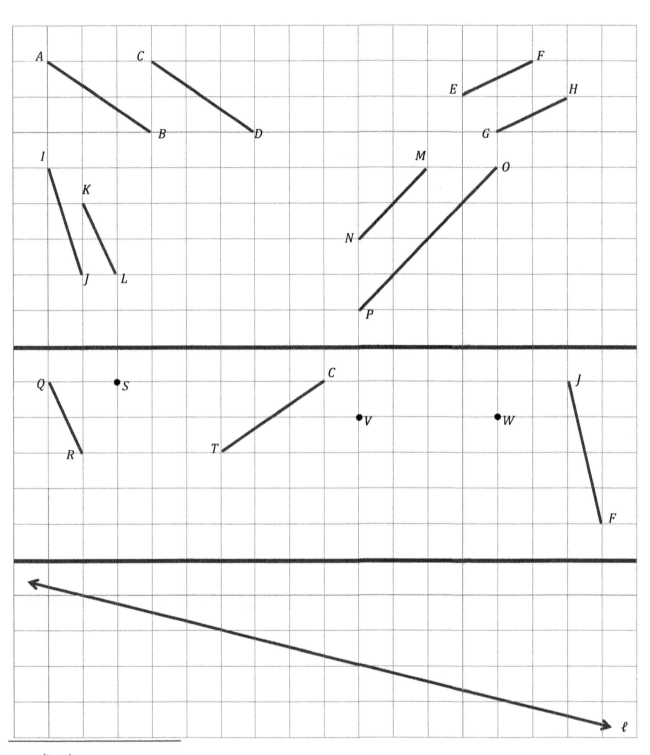

recording sheet

Lesson 13:   Construct parallel line segments on a rectangular grid.

78

Name _____   Date _____

1. Use the coordinate plane below to complete the following tasks.

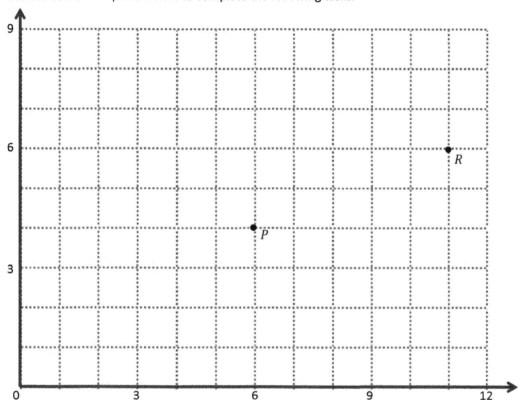

a. Identify the locations of P and R. P: (_____, _____) R: (_____, _____)
b. Draw $\overleftrightarrow{PR}$.
c. Plot the following coordinate pairs on the plane.

$$S: (6, 7) \qquad T: (11, 9)$$

d. Draw $\overleftrightarrow{ST}$.
e. Circle the relationship between $\overleftrightarrow{PR}$ and $\overleftrightarrow{ST}$. $\overleftrightarrow{PR} \perp \overleftrightarrow{ST}$ $\overleftrightarrow{PR} \parallel \overleftrightarrow{ST}$

f. Give the coordinates of a pair of points, U and V, such that $\overleftrightarrow{UV} \parallel \overleftrightarrow{PR}$.

$$U: (\_\_\_\_, \_\_\_\_) \qquad V: (\_\_\_\_, \_\_\_\_)$$

g. Draw $\overleftrightarrow{UV}$.

Lesson 14:   Construct parallel line segments, and analyze relationships of the coordinate pairs.

79

2. Use the coordinate plane below to complete the following tasks.

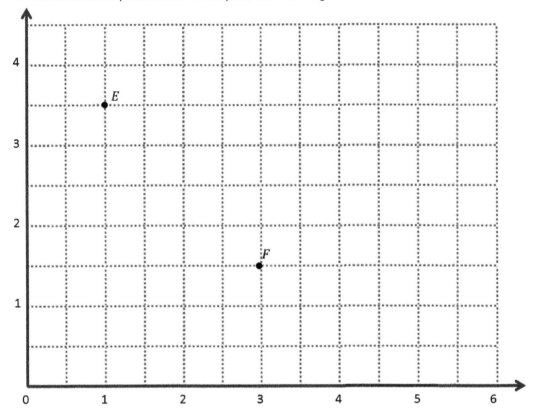

a. Identify the locations of E and F. E: (_____, _____) F: (_____, _____)

b. Draw $\overleftrightarrow{EF}$.

c. Generate coordinate pairs for L and M, such that $\overleftrightarrow{EF} \parallel \overleftrightarrow{LM}$.

   L: (_____, _____) M: (_____, _____)

d. Draw $\overleftrightarrow{LM}$.

e. Explain the pattern you made use of when generating coordinate pairs for L and M.

f. Give the coordinates of a point, H, such that $\overleftrightarrow{EF} \parallel \overleftrightarrow{GH}$.

   G: $(1\frac{1}{2}, 4)$ H: (_____, _____)

g. Explain how you chose the coordinates for H.

EUREKA
MATH™

Lesson 14: Construct parallel line segments, and analyze relationships of the coordinate pairs.

80

Name _____   Date _____

1. Use the coordinate plane below to complete the following tasks.

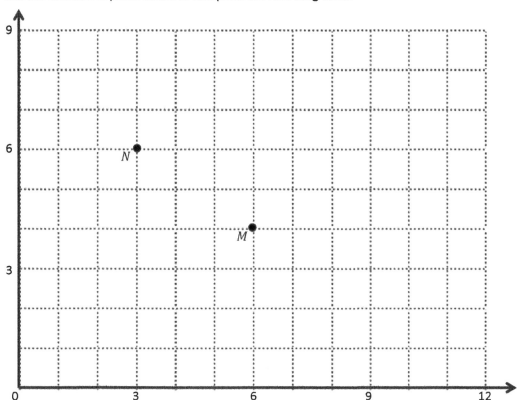

a. Identify the locations of M and N. M: (_____, _____) N: (_____, _____)

b. Draw $\overleftrightarrow{MN}$.

c. Plot the following coordinate pairs on the plane.

J: (5, 7) K: (8, 5)

d. Draw $\overleftrightarrow{JK}$.

e. Circle the relationship between $\overleftrightarrow{MN}$ and $\overleftrightarrow{JK}$. $\overleftrightarrow{MN} \perp \overleftrightarrow{JK}$ $\overleftrightarrow{MN} \parallel \overleftrightarrow{JK}$

f. Give the coordinates of a pair of points, F and G, such that $\overleftrightarrow{FG} \parallel \overleftrightarrow{MN}$.

F: (_____, _____) G: (_____, _____)

g. Draw $\overleftrightarrow{FG}$.

EUREKA
MATH™

Lesson 14:   Construct parallel line segments, and analyze relationships of the
             coordinate pairs.

81

2. Use the coordinate plane below to complete the following tasks.

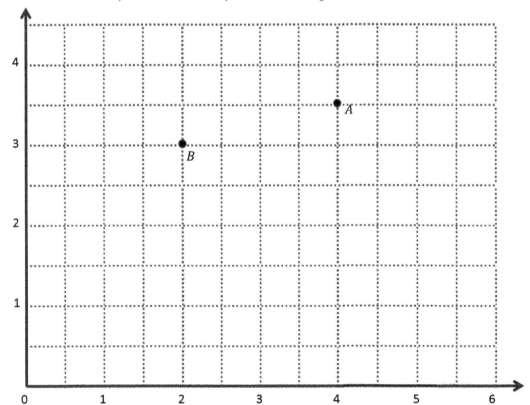

a. Identify the locations of A and B. A: (____ , ____) B: (____ , ____)

b. Draw $\overleftrightarrow{AB}$.

c. Generate coordinate pairs for C and D, such that $\overleftrightarrow{AB} \parallel \overleftrightarrow{CD}$.

    C: (____ , ____) D: (____ , ____)

d. Draw $\overleftrightarrow{CD}$.

e. Explain the pattern you used when generating coordinate pairs for C and D.

f. Give the coordinates of a point, F, such that $\overleftrightarrow{AB} \parallel \overleftrightarrow{EF}$.

    E: $(2\frac{1}{2}, 2\frac{1}{2})$ F: (____ , ____)

g. Explain how you chose the coordinates for F.

EUREKA
MATH™   Lesson 14:   Construct parallel line segments, and analyze relationships of the
                           coordinate pairs.

                                                                                                82

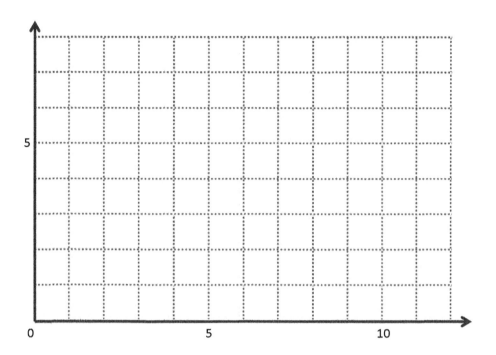

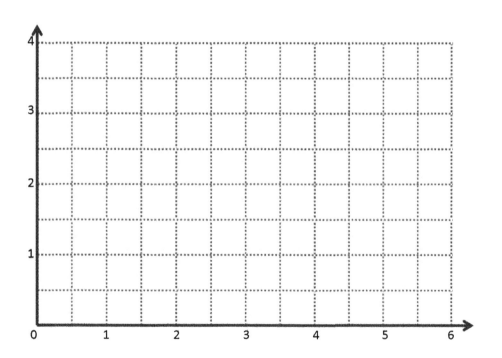

coordinate plane

EUREKA
MATH™

Lesson 14: Construct parallel line segments, and analyze relationships of the coordinate pairs.

83

Name _____   Date _____

1. Circle the pairs of segments that are perpendicular.

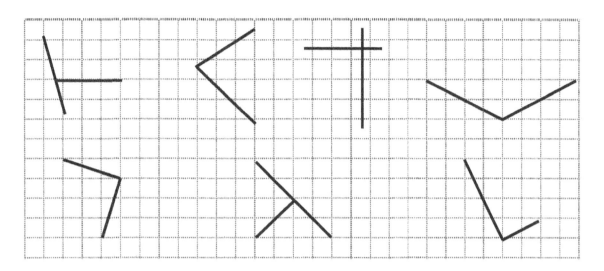

2. In the space below, use your right triangle templates to draw at least 3 different sets of perpendicular lines.

EUREKA
MATH™

Lesson 15:   Construct perpendicular line segments on a rectangular grid.

85

3. Draw a segment perpendicular to each given segment. Show your thinking by sketching triangles as needed.

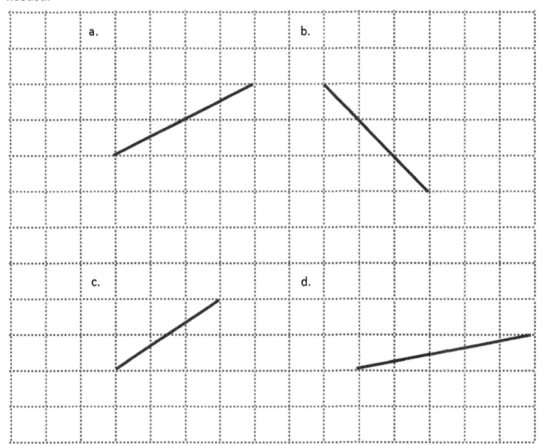

4. Draw 2 different lines perpendicular to line *e*.

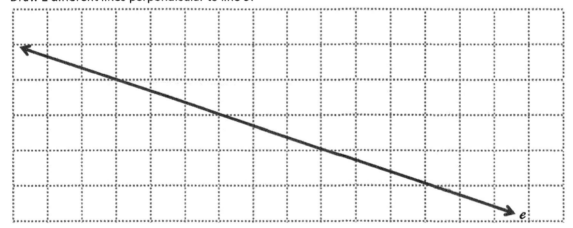

EUREKA MATH™   Lesson 15:   Construct perpendicular line segments on a rectangular grid.

86

Name _____   Date _____

1. Circle the pairs of segments that are perpendicular.

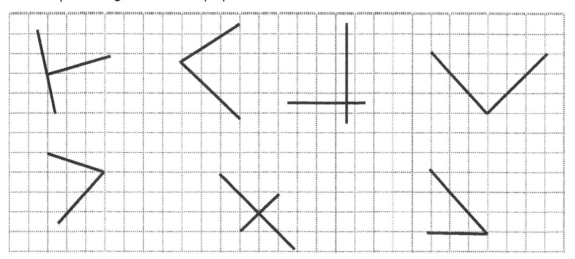

2. In the space below, use your right triangle templates to draw at least 3 different sets of perpendicular lines.

EUREKA
MATH™

Lesson 15:   Construct perpendicular line segments on a rectangular grid.

87

3. Draw a segment perpendicular to each given segment. Show your thinking by sketching triangles as needed.

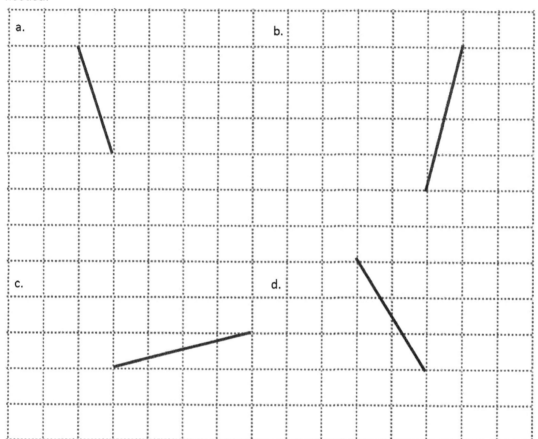

4. Draw 2 different lines perpendicular to line *b*.

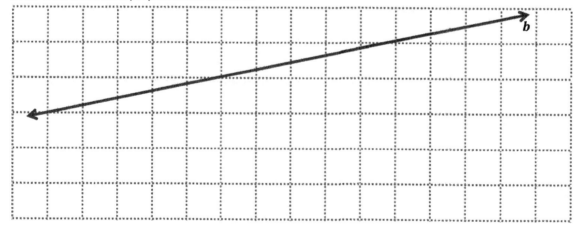

EUREKA
MATH™

Lesson 15:   Construct perpendicular line segments on a rectangular grid.

88

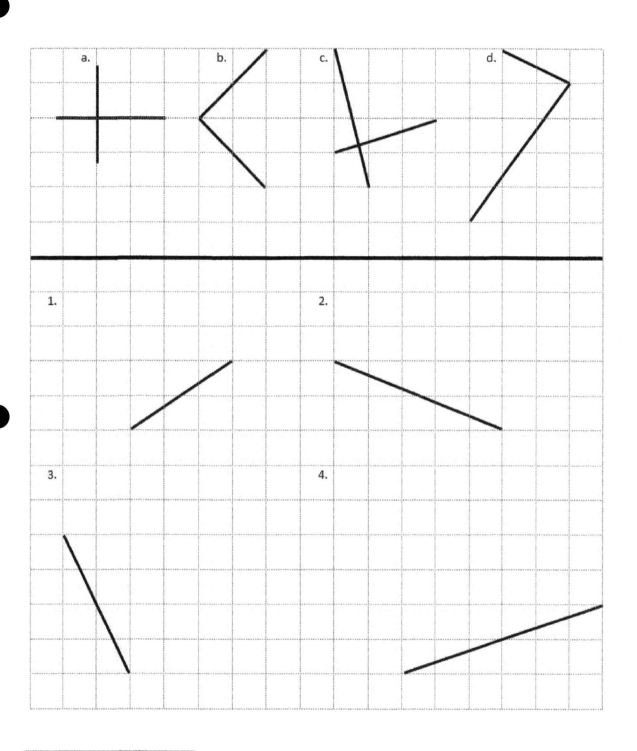

recording sheet

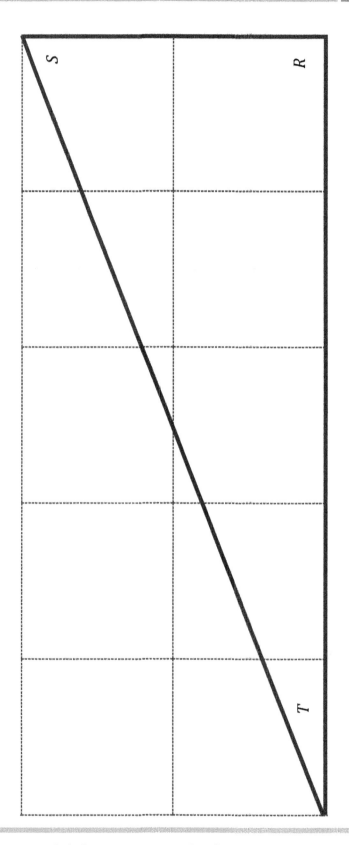

triangle *RST* (a)

EUREKA
MATH™

Lesson 15:   Construct perpendicular line segments on a rectangular grid.

90

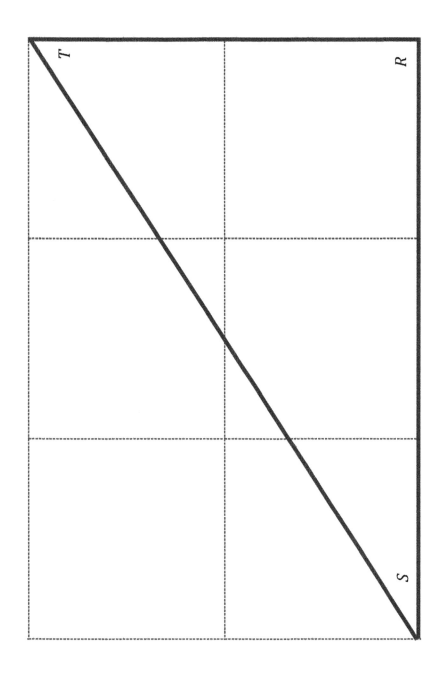

triangle RST (b)

Lesson 15:   Construct perpendicular line segments on a rectangular grid.

91

Name _____ Date _____

1. Use the coordinate plane below to complete the following tasks.

   a. Draw $\overline{AB}$.

   b. Plot point C $(0, 8)$.

   c. Draw $\overline{AC}$.

   d. Explain how you know $\angle CAB$ is a right angle without measuring it.

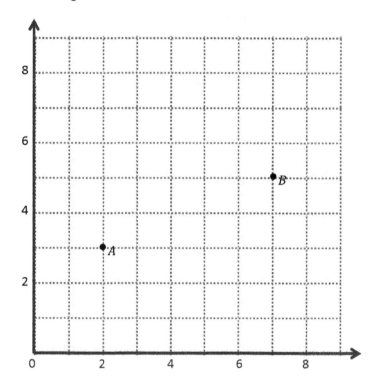

   e. Sean drew the picture to the right to find a segment perpendicular to $\overline{AB}$. Explain why Sean is correct.

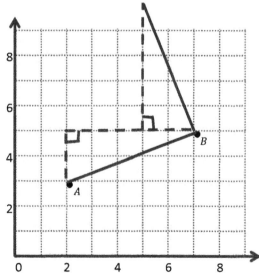

EUREKA MATH™

Lesson 16: Construct perpendicular line segments, and analyze relationships of the coordinate pairs.

93

2. Use the coordinate plane below to complete the following tasks.

    a. Draw $\overline{QT}$.

    b. Plot point $R\ (2, 6\frac{1}{2})$.

    c. Draw $\overline{QR}$.

    d. Explain how you know $\angle RQT$ is a right angle without measuring it.

    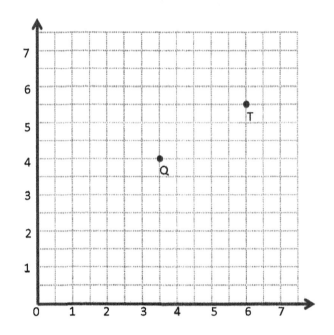

    e. Compare the coordinates of points Q and T. What is the difference of the x-coordinates? The y-coordinates?

    f. Compare the coordinates of points Q and R. What is the difference of the x-coordinates? The y-coordinates?

    g. What is the relationship of the differences you found in (e) and (f) to the triangles of which these two segments are a part?

3. $\overleftrightarrow{EF}$ contains the following points. E: (4, 1) F: (8, 7)

    Give the coordinates of a pair of points G and H, such that $\overleftrightarrow{EF} \perp \overleftrightarrow{GH}$.

    G: (_____, _____) H: (_____, _____)

EUREKA MATH   Lesson 16:   Construct perpendicular line segments, and analyze relationships of the coordinate pairs.

94

Name _____   Date _____

1. Use the coordinate plane below to complete the following tasks.

   a. Draw $\overline{PQ}$.

   b. Plot point R (3, 8).

   c. Draw $\overline{PR}$.

   d. Explain how you know ∠RPQ is a right angle without measuring it.

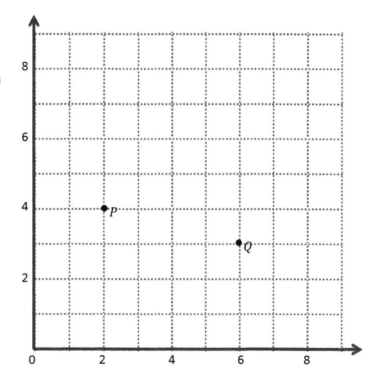

   e. Compare the coordinates of points P and Q. What is the difference of the x-coordinates? The y-coordinates?

   f. Compare the coordinates of points P and R. What is the difference of the x-coordinates? The y-coordinates?

   g. What is the relationship of the differences you found in (e) and (f) to the triangles of which these two segments are a part?

EUREKA
MATH™   Lesson 16:   Construct perpendicular line segments, and analyze relationships of
                             the coordinate pairs.

                                                                                              95

2. Use the coordinate plane below to complete the following tasks.

    a. Draw $\overline{CB}$.

    b. Plot point D $(\frac{1}{2}, 5\frac{1}{2})$.

    c. Draw $\overline{CD}$.

    d. Explain how you know $\angle DCB$ is a right angle without measuring it.

    e. Compare the coordinates of points C and B. What is the difference of the x-coordinates? The y-coordinates?

    f. Compare the coordinates of points C and D. What is the difference of the x-coordinates? The y-coordinates?

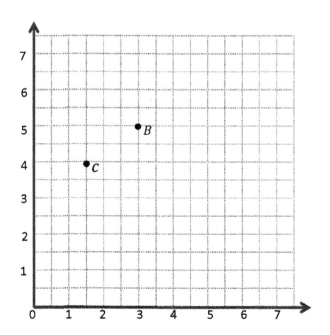

    g. What is the relationship of the differences you found in (e) and (f) to the triangles of which these two segments are a part?

3. $\overleftrightarrow{ST}$ contains the following points. S: (2, 3) T: (9, 6)

    Give the coordinates of a pair of points, U and V, such that $\overleftrightarrow{ST} \perp \overleftrightarrow{UV}$.

    U: (_____, _____) V: (_____, _____)

EUREKA
MATH™   Lesson 16:   Construct perpendicular line segments, and analyze relationships of
                              the coordinate pairs.

96

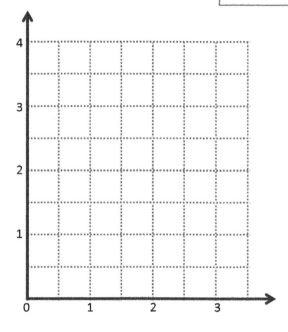

	(x, y)
A	
B	
C	

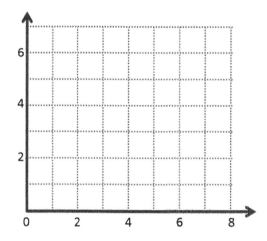

	(x, y)
D	
E	
F	

	(x, y)
G	
H	
I	

coordinate plane

EUREKA MATH™

Lesson 16:   Construct perpendicular line segments, and analyze relationships of the coordinate pairs.

97

Name _____ Date _____

1. Draw to create a figure that is symmetric about $\overleftrightarrow{AD}$.

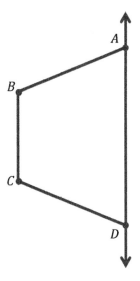

2. Draw precisely to create a figure that is symmetric about $\overleftrightarrow{HI}$.

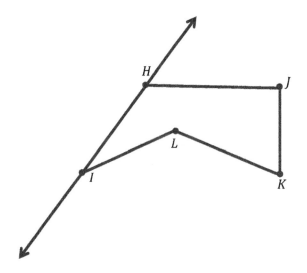

EUREKA
MATH™

Lesson 17: Draw symmetric figures using distance and angle measure from the line of symmetry.

99

3. Complete the following construction in the space below.

   a. Plot 3 non-collinear points, D, E, and F.

   b. Draw $\overline{DE}$, $\overline{EF}$, and $\overleftrightarrow{DF}$.

   c. Plot point G, and draw the remaining sides, such that quadrilateral $DEFG$ is symmetric about $\overleftrightarrow{DF}$.

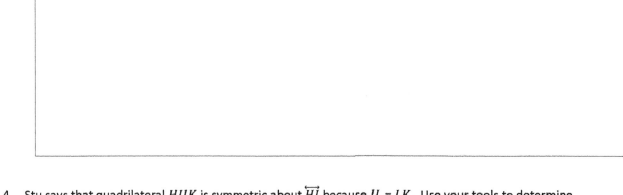

4. Stu says that quadrilateral $HIJK$ is symmetric about $\overleftrightarrow{HJ}$ because $IL = LK$. Use your tools to determine Stu's mistake. Explain your thinking.

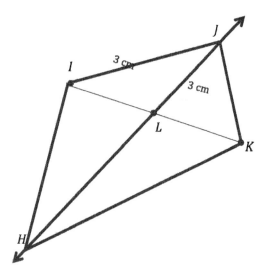

Name _____   Date _____

1. Draw to create a figure that is symmetric about $\overleftrightarrow{DE}$.

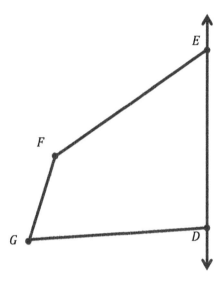

2. Draw to create a figure that is symmetric about $\overleftrightarrow{LM}$.

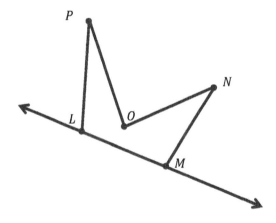

EUREKA
MATH™ | Lesson 17:   Draw symmetric figures using distance and angle measure from the
                             line of symmetry.

                                                                                      101

3. Complete the following construction in the space below.

    a.   Plot 3 non-collinear points, G, H, and I.

    b.   Draw $\overline{GH}$, $\overline{HI}$, and $\overleftrightarrow{IG}$.

    c.   Plot point J, and draw the remaining sides, such that quadrilateral $GHIJ$ is symmetric about $\overleftrightarrow{IG}$.

4. In the space below, use your tools to draw a symmetric figure about a line.

EUREKA
MATH

Lesson 17:   Draw symmetric figures using distance and angle measure from the line of symmetry.

102

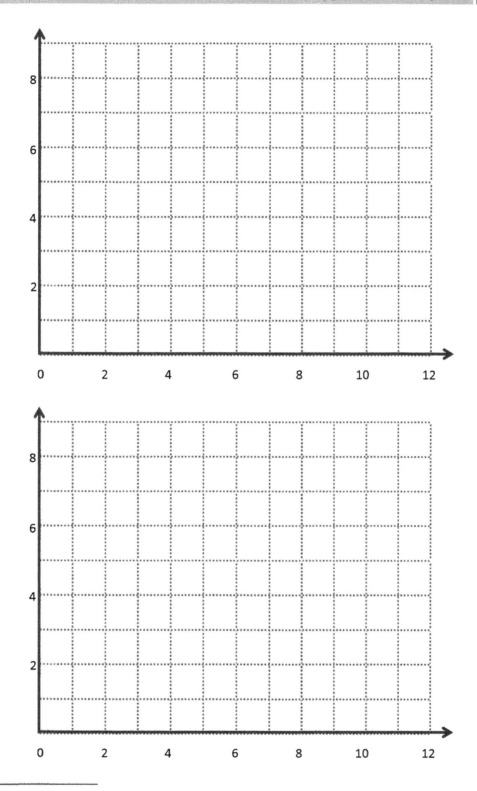

coordinate plane

Lesson 17:   Draw symmetric figures using distance and angle measure from the
              line of symmetry.

103

Name _____   Date _____

1. Use the plane to the right to complete the following tasks.
   a. Draw a line *t* whose rule is *y is always 0.7*.

   b. Plot the points from Table A on the grid in order. Then, draw line segments to connect the points.

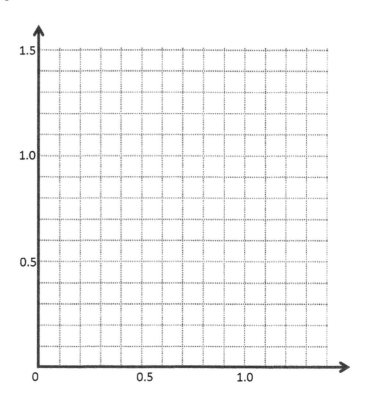

Table A

(x, y)
(0.1, 0.5)
(0.2, 0.3)
(0.3, 0.5)
(0.5, 0.1)
(0.6, 0.2)
(0.8, 0.2)
(0.9, 0.1)
(1.1, 0.5)
(1.2, 0.3)
(1.3, 0.5)

Table B

(x, y)

   c. Complete the drawing to create a figure that is symmetric about line *t*. For each point in Table A, record the corresponding point on the other side of the line of symmetry in Table B.

   d. Compare the *y*-coordinates in Table A with those in Table B. What do you notice?

   e. Compare the *x*-coordinates in Table A with those in Table B. What do you notice?

2. This figure has a second line of symmetry. Draw the line on the plane and write the rule for this line.

EUREKA MATH™   Lesson 18:   Draw symmetric figures on the coordinate plane.

105

3. Use the plane below to complete the following tasks.

    a. Draw a line **u** whose rule is y *is equal to* $x + \frac{1}{4}$.

    b. Construct a figure with a total of 6 points, all on the same side of the line.

    c. Record the coordinates of each point, in the order in which they were drawn, in Table A.

    d. Swap your paper with a neighbor and have him or her complete parts e–f, below.

Table A   **Table B**

(x, y)

(x, y)

    e. Complete the drawing to create a figure that is symmetric about **u**. For each point in Table A, record the corresponding point on the other side of the line of symmetry in Table B.

    f. Explain how you found the points symmetric to your partner's about **u**.

EUREKA MATH   Lesson 18:   Draw symmetric figures on the coordinate plane.

106

Name _____   Date _____

1. Use the plane to the right to complete the following tasks.

    a. Draw a line **s** whose rule is *x is always 5*.

    b. Plot the points from Table A on the grid in order. Then, draw
        line segments to connect the points in order.

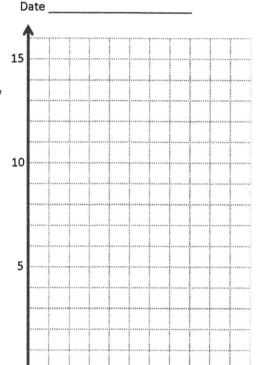

Table A

(x, y)
(1, 13)
(1, 12)
(2, 10)
(4, 9)
(4, 3)
(1, 2)
(5, 2)

Table B

(x, y)

c. Complete the drawing to create a figure that is symmetric about line **s**. For each point in Table A, record the symmetric point on the other side of **s**.

d. Compare the *y*-coordinates in Table A with those in Table B. What do you notice?

e. Compare the *x*-coordinates in Table A with those in Table B. What do you notice?

EUREKA MATH™ | **Lesson 18:**   Draw symmetric figures on the coordinate plane.

107

2. Use the plane to the right to complete the following tasks.

    a. Draw a line p whose rule is, *y is equal to x.*

    b. Plot the points from Table A on the grid in order. Then, draw line segments to connect the points.

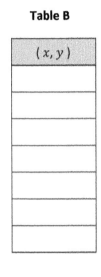

Table A

(x, y)
$(\frac{1}{2}, \frac{1}{2})$
$(1, 2)$
$(1\frac{1}{2}, 1\frac{1}{2})$
$(2, 4)$
$(3\frac{1}{2}, 3\frac{1}{2})$
$(4, 4\frac{1}{2})$
$(5, 5)$

Table B

(x, y)

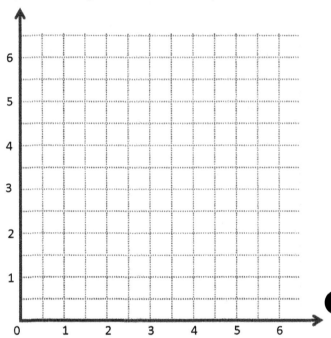

    c. Complete the drawing to create a figure that is symmetric about line p. For each point in Table A, record the symmetric point on the other side of the line p in Table B.

    d. Compare the y-coordinates in Table A with those in Table B. What do you notice?

    e. Compare the x-coordinates in Table A with those in Table B. What do you notice?

EUREKA MATH™   Lesson 18:   Draw symmetric figures on the coordinate plane.

108

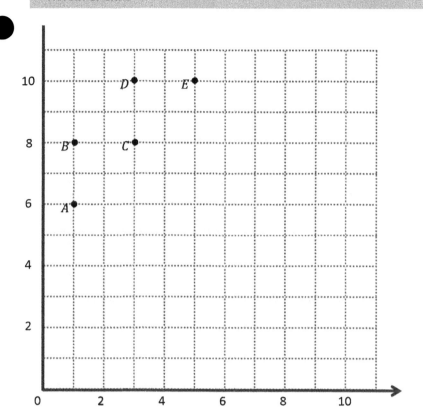

Table A

Point	(x, y)
A	
B	
C	
D	
E	

Table C

(x, y)

Table B

Point	(x, y)
I	
H	
G	
F	

Table D

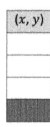

Table E

Point	(x, y)
A	$(1, 1)$
B	$(1\frac{1}{2}, 3\frac{1}{2})$
C	$(2, 3)$
D	$(2\frac{1}{2}, 3\frac{1}{2})$
E	$(2\frac{1}{2}, 2\frac{1}{2})$
F	$(3\frac{1}{2}, 2\frac{1}{2})$
G	$(3, 2)$
H	$(3\frac{1}{2}, 1\frac{1}{2})$

coordinate plane

EUREKA
MATH™

Lesson 18:   Draw symmetric figures on the coordinate plane.

Name _____ Date _____

1. The line graph below tracks the rain accumulation, measured every half hour, during a rainstorm that began at 2:00 p.m. and ended at 7:00 p.m. Use the information in the graph to answer the questions that follow.

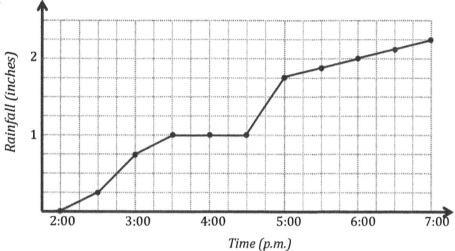

a. How many inches of rain fell during this five-hour period?

b. During which half-hour period did $\frac{1}{2}$ inch rain fall? Explain how you know.

c. During which half-hour period did rain fall most rapidly? Explain how you know.

d. Why do you think the line is horizontal between 3:30 p.m. and 4:30 p.m.?

e. For every inch of rain that fell here, a nearby community in the mountains received a foot and a half of snow. How many inches of snow fell in the mountain community between 5:00 p.m. and 7:00 p.m.?

2. Mr. Boyd checks the gauge on his home's fuel tank on the first day of every month. The line graph to the right was created using the data he collected.

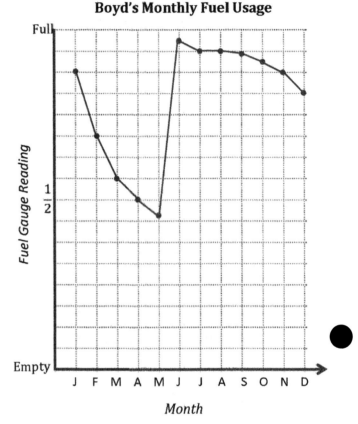

Boyd's Monthly Fuel Usage

a. According to the graph, during which month(s) does the amount of fuel decrease most rapidly?

b. The Boyds took a month-long vacation. During which month did this most likely occur? Explain how you know using the data in the graph.

c. Mr. Boyd's fuel company filled his tank once this year. During which month did this most likely occur? Explain how you know.

d. The Boyd family's fuel tank holds 284 gallons of fuel when full. How many gallons of fuel did the Boyds use in February?

e. Mr. Boyd pays $3.54 per gallon of fuel. What is the cost of the fuel used in February and March?

Name _____   Date _____

1. The line graph below tracks the balance of Howard's checking account, at the end of each day, between May 12 and May 26. Use the information in the graph to answer the questions that follow.

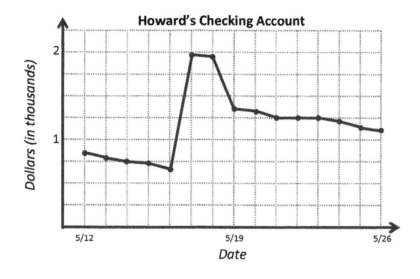

a. About how much money does Howard have in his checking account on May 21?

b. If Howard spends $250 from his checking account on May 26, about how much money will he have left in his account?

c. Explain what happened with Howard's money between May 21 and May 23.

d. Howard received a payment from his job that went directly into his checking account. On which day did this most likely occur? Explain how you know.

e. Howard bought a new television during the time shown in the graph. On which day did this most likely occur? Explain how you know.

2. The line graph below tracks Santino's time at the beginning and end of each part of a triathlon. Use the information in the graph to answer the questions that follow.

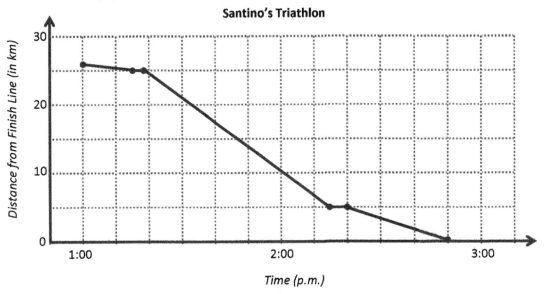

a. How long does it take Santino to finish the triathlon?

b. To complete the triathlon, Santino first swims across a lake, then bikes through the city, and finishes by running around the lake. According to the graph, what was the distance of the running portion of the race?

c. During the race, Santino pauses to put on his biking shoes and helmet, and then later to change into his running shoes. At what times did this most likely occur? Explain how you know.

d. Which part of the race does Santino finish most quickly? How do you know?

e. During which part of the triathlon is Santino racing most quickly? Explain how you know.

EUREKA MATH   Lesson 19:   Plot data on line graphs and analyze trends.

114

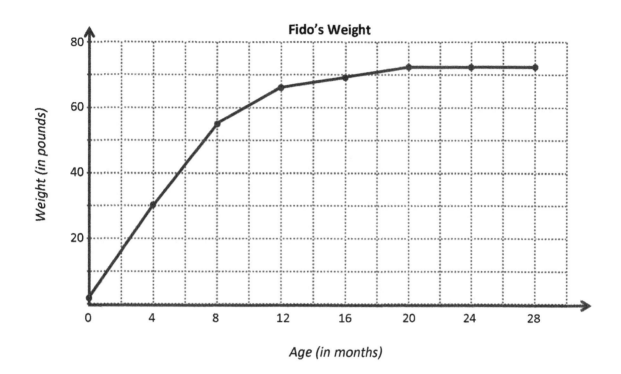

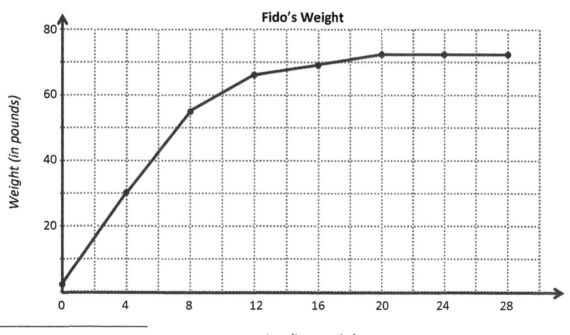

line graph practice sheet

Name _____   Date _____

1. The line graph below tracks the total tomato production for one tomato plant. The total tomato
    production is plotted at the end of each of 8 weeks. Use the information in the graph to answer the
    questions that follow.

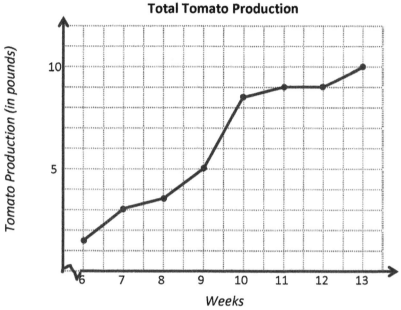

Total Tomato Production

a. How many pounds of tomatoes did this plant produce at the end of 13 weeks?

b. How many pounds of tomatoes did this plant produce from Week 7 to Week 11? Explain how you
    know.

c. Which one-week period showed the greatest change in tomato production? The least? Explain how
    you know.

d. During Weeks 6–8, Jason fed the tomato plant just water. During Weeks 8–10, he used a mixture of
    water and Fertilizer A, and in Weeks 10–13, he used water and Fertilizer B on the tomato plant.
    Compare the tomato production for these periods of time.

EUREKA MATH   Lesson 20:   Use coordinate systems to solve real world problems.

117

2. Use the story context below to sketch a line graph. Then, answer the questions that follow.

The number of fifth-grade students attending Magnolia School has changed over time. The school opened in 2006 with 156 students in the fifth grade. The student population grew the same amount each year before reaching its largest class of 210 students in 2008. The following year, Magnolia lost one-seventh of its fifth graders. In 2010, the enrollment dropped to 154 students and remained constant in 2011. For the next two years, the enrollment grew by 7 students each year.

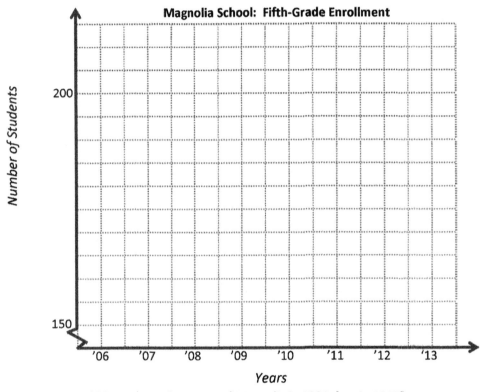

a. How many more fifth-grade students attend Magnolia in 2009 than in 2013?

b. Between which two consecutive years was there the greatest change in student population?

c. If the fifth-grade population continues to grow in the same pattern as in 2012 and 2013, in what year will the number of students match 2008's enrollment?

Lesson 20:   Use coordinate systems to solve real world problems.

118

Name _____   Date _____

Use the graph to answer the questions.

Johnny left his home at 6 a.m. and kept track of the number of kilometers he traveled at the end of each hour of his trip. He recorded the data in a line graph.

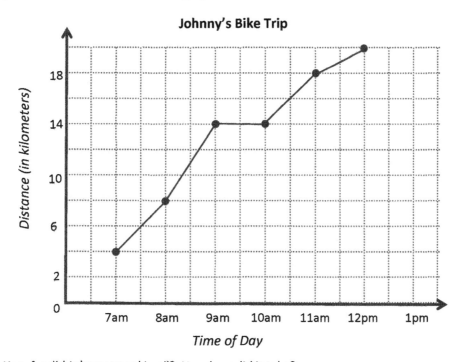

a. How far did Johnny travel in all? How long did it take?

b. Johnny took a one-hour break to have a snack and take some pictures. What time did he stop? How do you know?

c. Did Johnny cover more distance before his break or after? Explain.

d. Between which two hours did Johnny ride 4 kilometers?

e. During which hour did Johnny ride the fastest? Explain how you know.

   Lesson 20:   Use coordinate systems to solve real world problems.

120

Student _____ Team _____ Date _____ Problem 1

Pierre's Paper

Pierre folded a square piece of paper vertically to make two rectangles. Each rectangle had a perimeter of 39 inches. How long is each side of the original square? What is the area of the original square? What is the area of one of the rectangles?

Student _____ Team _____ Date _____ Problem 2

Shopping with Elise

Elise saved $184. She bought a scarf, a necklace, and a notebook. After her purchases, she still had $39.50. The scarf cost three-fifths the cost of the necklace, and the notebook was one-sixth as much as the scarf. What was the cost of each item? How much more did the necklace cost than the notebook?

Lesson 21:   Make sense of complex, multi-step problems, and persevere in solving them. Share and critique peer solutions.

Student _____ Team _____ Date _____ Problem 3

The Hewitt's Carpet

The Hewitt family is buying carpet for two rooms. The dining room is a square that measures 12 feet on each side. The den is 9 yards by 5 yards. Mrs. Hewitt has budgeted $2,650 for carpeting both rooms. The green carpet she is considering costs $42.75 per square yard, and the brown carpet's price is $4.95 per square foot. What are the ways she can carpet the rooms and stay within her budget?

Student _____ Team _____ Date _____ Problem 4

AAA Taxi

AAA Taxi charges $1.75 for the first mile and $1.05 for each additional mile. How far could Mrs. Leslie travel for $20 if she tips the cab driver $2.50?

EUREKA MATH | **Lesson 21:** Make sense of complex, multi-step problems, and persevere in solving them. Share and critique peer solutions.

122

Student _____ Team _____ Date _____ Problem 5

Pumpkins and Squash

Three pumpkins and two squash weigh 27.5 pounds. Four pumpkins and three squash weigh 37.5 pounds. Each pumpkin weighs the same as the other pumpkins, and each squash weighs the same as the other squash. How much does each pumpkin weigh? How much does each squash weigh?

Student _____ Team _____ Date _____ Problem 6

Toy Cars and Trucks

Henry had 20 convertibles and 5 trucks in his miniature car collection. After Henry's aunt bought him some more miniature trucks, Henry found that one-fifth of his collection consisted of convertibles. How many trucks did his aunt buy?

Lesson 21: Make sense of complex, multi-step problems, and persevere in solving them. Share and critique peer solutions.

Student _____ Team _____ Date _____ Problem 7

Pairs of Scouts

Some girls in a Girl Scout troop are pairing up with some boys in a Boy Scout troop to practice square dancing. Two-thirds of the girls are paired with three-fifths of the boys. What fraction of the scouts is square dancing?

(Each pair is one Girl Scout and one Boy Scout. The pairs are only from these two troops.)

Student _____ Team _____ Date _____ Problem 8

Sandra's Measuring Cups

Sandra is making cookies that require $5\frac{1}{2}$ cups of oatmeal. She has only two measuring cups: a one-half cup and a three-fourths cup. What is the smallest number of scoops that she could make in order to get $5\frac{1}{2}$ cups?

EUREKA
MATH™
Lesson 21:   Make sense of complex, multi-step problems, and persevere in solving
              them. Share and critique peer solutions.

Student _____ Team _____ Date _____ Problem 9

Blue Squares

The dimensions of each successive blue square pictured to the right are half that of the previous blue square. The lower left blue square measures 6 inches by 6 inches.

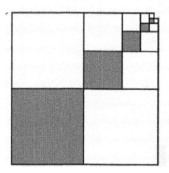

    a. Find the area of the shaded part.

    b. Find the total area of the shaded and unshaded parts.

    c. What fraction of the figure is shaded?

Lesson 21:   Make sense of complex, multi-step problems, and persevere in solving
              them. Share and critique peer solutions.

                                                                                            125

Name _____   Date _____

1. Sara travels twice as far as Eli when going to camp. Ashley travels as far as Sara and Eli together. Hazel travels 3 times as far as Sara. In total, all four travel 888 miles to camp. How far does each of them travel?

Lesson 21:   Make sense of complex, multi-step problems, and persevere in solving them. Share and critique peer solutions.

126

The following problem is a brainteaser for your enjoyment. It is intended to encourage working together and family problem-solving fun. It is not a required element of this homework assignment.

2. A man wants to take a goat, a bag of cabbage, and a wolf over to an island. His boat will only hold him and one animal or item. If the goat is left with the cabbage, he'll eat it. If the wolf is left with the goat, he'll eat it. How can the man transport all three to the island without anything being eaten?

EUREKA MATH   Lesson 21:   Make sense of complex, multi-step problems, and persevere in solving them. Share and critique peer solutions.

127

Name _____   Date _____

Solve using any method. Show all your thinking.

1. Study this diagram showing all squares. Fill in the table.

Figure	Area in Square Feet
1	1 ft^2
2	
3	
4	9 ft^2
5	
6	1 ft^2
7	
8	
9	
10	
11	

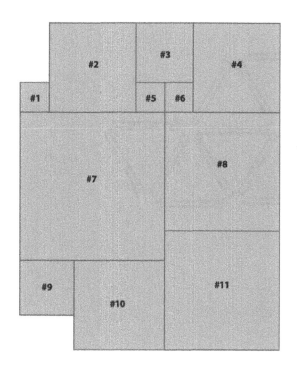

Lesson 22:   Make sense of complex, multi-step problems, and persevere in solving them. Share and critique peer solutions.

129

The following problem is a brainteaser for your enjoyment. It is intended to encourage working together and family problem-solving fun. It is not a required element of this homework assignment.

2. Remove 3 matches to leave 3 triangles.

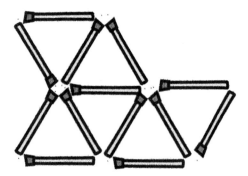

Lesson 22: Make sense of complex, multi-step problems, and persevere in solving them. Share and critique peer solutions.

130

Name _____   Date _____

1. In the diagram, the length of Figure S is $\frac{2}{3}$ the length of Figure T. If S has an area of 368 cm², find the
    perimeter of the figure.

| S | T | ⊢16 cm |

   EUREKA
MATH | Lesson 23:   Make sense of complex, multi-step problems, and persevere in solving
                        them. Share and critique peer solutions   131

The following problems are puzzles for your enjoyment. They are intended to encourage working together and family problem-solving fun and are not a required element of this homework assignment.

2. Take 12 matchsticks arranged in a grid as shown below, and remove 2 matchsticks so 2 squares remain. How can you do this? Draw the new arrangement.

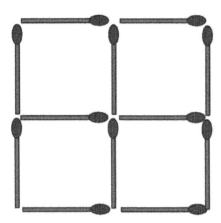

3. Moving only 3 matchsticks makes the fish turn around and swim the opposite way. Which matchsticks did you move? Draw the new shape.

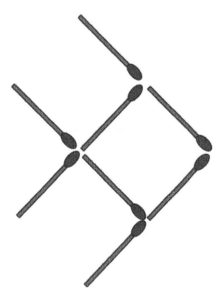

Lesson 23: Make sense of complex, multi-step problems, and persevere in solving them. Share and critique peer solutions

132

Name _____   Date _____

1. Pat's Potato Farm grew 490 pounds of potatoes. Pat delivered $\frac{3}{7}$ of the potatoes to a vegetable stand. The owner of the vegetable stand delivered $\frac{2}{3}$ of the potatoes he bought to a local grocery store, which packaged half of the potatoes that were delivered into 5-pound bags. How many 5-pound bags did the grocery store package?

Lesson 24:   Make sense of complex, multi-step problems, and persevere in solving them. Share and critique peer solutions.

133

The following problems are for your enjoyment. They are intended to encourage working together and family problem-solving fun. They are not a required element of this homework assignment.

2. Six matchsticks are arranged into an equilateral triangle. How can you arrange them into 4 equilateral triangles without breaking or overlapping any of them? Draw the new shape.

3. Kenny's dog, Charlie, is really smart! Last week, Charlie buried 7 bones in all. He buried them in 5 straight lines and put 3 bones in each line. How is this possible? Sketch how Charlie buried the bones.

Lesson 24:   Make sense of complex, multi-step problems, and persevere in solving them. Share and critique peer solutions.

134

Name _____ Date _____

1. Fred and Ethyl had 132 flowers altogether at first. After Fred sold $\frac{1}{4}$ of his flowers and Ethyl sold 48 of her flowers, they had the same number of flowers left. How many flowers did each of them have at first?

Lesson 25: Make sense of complex, multi-step problems, and perservere in solving them. Critique and share peer solutions..

135

The following problems are puzzles for your enjoyment. They are intended to encourage working together and family problem-solving fun. They are not a required element of this homework assignment.

2. Without removing any, move 2 matchsticks to make 4 identical squares. Which matchsticks did you move? Draw the new shape.

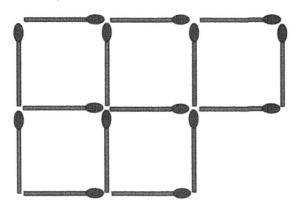

3. Move 3 matchsticks to form exactly (and only) 3 identical squares. Which matchsticks did you move? Draw the new shape.

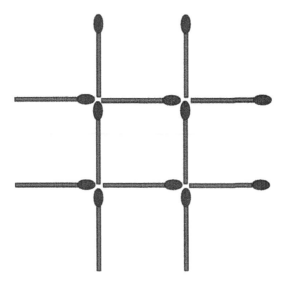

Lesson 25:   Make sense of complex, multi-step problems, and perservere in solving them. Critique and share peer solutions..

136

Name _____   Date _____

1. For each written phrase, write a numerical expression, and then evaluate your expression.

a. Three fifths of the sum of thirteen and six

Numerical expression:

Solution:

b. Subtract four thirds from one seventh of sixty-three

Numerical expression:

Solution:

c. Six copies of the sum of nine fifths and three

Numerical expression:

Solution:

d. Three fourths of the product of four fifths and fifteen

Numerical expression:

Solution:

2. Write at least 2 numerical expressions for each phrase below. Then, solve.

   a. Two thirds of eight

   b. One sixth of the product of four and nine

3. Use <, >, or = to make true number sentences without calculating. Explain your thinking.

   a. $217 \times \left(42 + \frac{48}{5}\right)$ $(217 \times 42) + \frac{48}{5}$

   b. $\left(687 \times \frac{3}{16}\right) \times \frac{7}{12}$ $\left(687 \times \frac{3}{16}\right) \times \frac{3}{12}$

   c. $5 \times 3.76 + 5 \times 2.68$ 5×6.99

Name _____ Date _____

1. For each written phrase, write a numerical expression, and then evaluate your expression.

a. Forty times the sum of forty-three and fifty-seven

Numerical expression:

Solution:

b. Divide the difference between one thousand three hundred and nine hundred fifty by four

Numerical expression:

Solution:

c. Seven times the quotient of five and seven

Numerical expression:

Solution:

d. One fourth the difference of four sixths and three twelfths

Numerical expression:

Solution:

2. Write at least 2 numerical expressions for each written phrase below. Then, solve.

   a. Three fifths of seven

   b. One sixth the product of four and eight

3. Use <, >, or = to make true number sentences without calculating. Explain your thinking.

   a.   4 tenths + 3 tens + 1 thousandth ◯ 30.41

   b. $\left(5 \times \frac{1}{10}\right) + \left(7 \times \frac{1}{1000}\right)$ ◯ 0.507

   c.   8 × 7.20 ◯ 8 × 4.36 + 8 × 3.59

EUREKA MATH   Lesson 26: Solidify writing and interpreting numerical expressions.

140

		forty-three less than three fifths of the product of ten and twenty	five sixths the difference of three hundred twenty-nine and two hundred eighty-one
six sevenths of nine	two thirds the sum of twenty-three and fifty-seven		
three times as much as the sum of three fourths and two thirds	the difference between thirty thirties and twenty-eight thirties	twenty-seven more than half the sum of four and one eighth and six and two thirds	the sum of eighty-eight and fifty-six divided by twelve
the product of nine and eight divided by four	one sixth the product of twelve and four	six copies of the sum of six twelfths and three fourths	double three fourths of eighteen

expression cards

$96 \times (63 + \frac{17}{12})$ $(96 \times 63) + \frac{17}{12}$

$(437 \times \frac{9}{15}) \times \frac{6}{8}$ $(437 \times \frac{9}{15}) \times \frac{7}{8}$

$4 \times 8.35 + 4 \times 6.21$ 4×15.87

$\frac{6}{7} \times (3{,}065 + 4{,}562)$ $(3{,}065 + 4{,}562) + \frac{6}{7}$

$(8.96 \times 3) + (5.07 \times 8)$ ◯ $(8.96 + 3) \times (5.07 + 8)$

$(297 \times \frac{16}{15}) + \frac{8}{3}$ ◯ $(297 \times \frac{13}{15}) + \frac{8}{3}$

$\frac{12}{7} \times (\frac{5}{4} + \frac{5}{9})$ ◯ $\frac{12}{7} \times \frac{5}{4} + \frac{12}{7} \times \frac{5}{9}$

comparing expressions game board

Name _____   Date _____

1. Use the RDW process to solve the word problems below.

    a. Julia completes her homework in an hour. She spends $\frac{7}{12}$ of the time doing her math homework and $\frac{1}{6}$ of the time practicing her spelling words. The rest of the time she spends reading. How many minutes does Julia spend reading?

    b. Fred has 36 marbles. Elise has $\frac{8}{9}$ as many marbles as Fred. Annika has $\frac{3}{4}$ as many marbles as Elise. How many marbles does Annika have?

EUREKA
MATH   **Lesson 27:**   Solidify writing and interpreting numerical expressions.

                                                                                143

2. Write and solve a word problem that might be solved using the expressions in the chart below.

Expression	Word Problem	Solution
$\frac{2}{3} \times 18$		
$(26 + 34) \times \frac{5}{6}$		
$7 - \left(\frac{5}{12} + \frac{1}{2}\right)$		

Name _____   Date _____

1. Use the RDW process to solve the word problems below.

   a. There are 36 students in Mr. Meyer's class. Of those students, $\frac{5}{12}$ played tag at recess, $\frac{1}{3}$ played kickball, and the rest played basketball. How many students in Mr. Meyer's class played basketball?

   b. Julie brought 24 apples to school to share with her classmates. Of those apples, $\frac{2}{3}$ are red and the rest are green. Julie's classmates ate $\frac{3}{4}$ of the red apples and $\frac{1}{2}$ of the green apples. How many apples are left?

Lesson 27:   Solidify writing and interpreting numerical expressions.

2. Write and solve a word problem for each expression in the chart below.

Expression	Word Problem	Solution
$144 \times \dfrac{7}{12}$		
$9 - \left(\dfrac{4}{9} + \dfrac{1}{3} \right)$		
$\dfrac{3}{4} \times (36 + 12)$		

Name _____   Date _____

1. Answer the following questions about fluency.

    a. What does being fluent with a math skill mean to you?

    b. Why is fluency with certain math skills important?

    c. With which math skills do you think you should be fluent?

    d. With which math skills do you feel most fluent? Least fluent?

    e. How can you continue to improve your fluency?

EUREKA
MATH™ | Lesson 28:   Solidify fluency with Grade 5 skills.

147

2. Use the chart below to list skills from today's activities with which you are fluent.

Fluent Skills

3. Use the chart below to list skills we practiced today with which you are less fluent.

Skills to Practice More

Name _____   Date _____

1. Use what you learned about your fluency skills today to answer the questions below.

    a. Which skills should you practice this summer to maintain and build your fluency? Why?

    b. Write a goal for yourself about a skill that you want to work on this summer.

    c. Explain the steps you can take to reach your goal.

    d. How will reaching this goal help you as a math student?

EUREKA
MATH™   Lesson 28:   Solidify fluency with Grade 5 skills.

149

2. In the chart below, plan a new fluency activity that you can play at home this summer to help you build or maintain a skill that you listed in Problem 1(a). When planning your activity, be sure to think about the factors listed below:

- The materials that you'll need.
- Who can play with you (if more than 1 player is needed).
- The usefulness of the activity for building your skills.

Skill:
Name of Activity:
Materials Needed:
Description:

Write Fractions as Mixed Numbers

Materials: (S) Personal white board

T: (Write $\frac{13}{2}$ = _____ ÷ _____ = _____.) Write the fraction as a division problem and mixed number.

S: (Write $\frac{13}{2}$ = 13 ÷ 2 = $6\frac{1}{2}$.)

More practice!

$\frac{11}{2}$, $\frac{17}{2}$, $\frac{44}{2}$, $\frac{31}{10}$, $\frac{23}{10}$, $\frac{47}{10}$, $\frac{89}{10}$, $\frac{8}{3}$, $\frac{13}{3}$, $\frac{26}{3}$, $\frac{9}{4}$, $\frac{13}{4}$, $\frac{15}{4}$, and $\frac{35}{4}$.

Fraction of a Set

Materials: (S) Personal white board

T: (Write $\frac{1}{2}$ × 10.) Draw a tape diagram to model the whole number.

S: (Draw a tape diagram, and label it 10.)

T: Draw a line to split the tape diagram in half.

S: (Draw a line.)

T: What is the value of each part of your tape diagram?

S: 5.

T: So, what is $\frac{1}{2}$ of 10?

S: 5.

More practice!

$8 \times \frac{1}{2}$, $8 \times \frac{1}{4}$, $6 \times \frac{1}{3}$, $30 \times \frac{1}{6}$, $42 \times \frac{1}{7}$, $42 \times \frac{1}{6}$, $48 \times \frac{1}{8}$, $54 \times \frac{1}{9}$, and $54 \times \frac{1}{6}$.

Convert to Hundredths

Materials: (S) Personal white board

T: (Write $\frac{3}{4}$ = $\frac{\ }{100}$.) 4 times what factor equals 100?

S: 25.

T: Write the equivalent fraction.

S: (Write $\frac{3}{4}$ = $\frac{75}{100}$.)

More practice!

$\frac{3}{4}$ = $\frac{\ }{100}$, $\frac{1}{50}$ = $\frac{\ }{100}$, $\frac{3}{50}$ = $\frac{\ }{100}$, $\frac{1}{20}$ = $\frac{\ }{100}$, $\frac{3}{20}$ = $\frac{\ }{100}$,

$\frac{1}{25}$ = $\frac{\ }{100}$, and $\frac{2}{25}$ = $\frac{\ }{100}$.

Multiply a Fraction and a Whole Number

Materials: (S) Personal white board

T: (Write $\frac{8}{4}$.) Write the corresponding division sentence.

S: (Write 8 ÷ 4 = 2.)

T: (Write $\frac{1}{4}$ × 8.) Write the complete multiplication sentence.

S: (Write $\frac{1}{4}$ × 8 = 2.)

More practice!

$\frac{18}{6}$, $\frac{15}{3}$, $\frac{18}{3}$, $\frac{27}{9}$, $\frac{54}{6}$, $\frac{51}{3}$, and $\frac{63}{7}$.

fluency activities

Multiply Mentally

Materials: (S) Personal white board

T: (Write 9 × 10.) On your personal white board, write the complete multiplication sentence.
S: (Write 9 × 10 = 90.)
T: (Write 9 × 9 = 90 – _____ below 9 × 10 = 90.) Write the number sentence, filling in the blank.
S: (Write 9 × 9 = 90 – 9.)
T: 9 × 9 is…?
S: 81.

More practice!

9 × 99, 15 × 9, and 29 × 99.

One Unit More

Materials: (S) Personal white board

T: (Write 5 tenths.) On your personal white board, write the decimal that's one-tenth more than 5 tenths.
S: (Write 0.6.)

More practice!

5 hundredths, 5 thousandths, 8 hundredths, and 2 thousandths. Specify the unit of increase.

T: (Write 0.052.) Write one more thousandth.
S: (Write 0.053.)

More practice!

1 tenth more than 35 hundredths,
1 thousandth more than 35 hundredths, and
1 hundredth more than 438 thousandths.

Find the Product

Materials: (S) Personal white board

T: (Write 4 × 3.) Complete the multiplication sentence giving the second factor in unit form.
S: (Write 4 × 3 ones = 12 ones.)
T: (Write 4 × 0.2.) Complete the multiplication sentence giving the second factor in unit form.
S: (Write 4 × 2 tenths = 8 tenths.)
T: (Write 4 × 3.2.) Complete the multiplication sentence giving the second factor in unit form.
S: (Write 4 × 3 ones 2 tenths = 12 ones 8 tenths.)
T: Write the complete multiplication sentence.
S: (Write 4 × 3.2 = 12.8.)

More practice!

4 × 3.21, 9 × 2, 9 × 0.1, 9 × 0.03, 9 × 2.13, 4.012 × 4, and 5 × 3.2375.

Add and Subtract Decimals

Materials: (S) Personal white board

T: (Write 7 ones + 258 thousandths + 1 hundredth = _____.) Write the addition sentence in decimal form.
S: (Write 7 + 0.258 + 0.01 = 7.268.)

More practice!

7 ones + 258 thousandths + 3 hundredths,
6 ones + 453 thousandths + 4 hundredths,
2 ones + 37 thousandths + 5 tenths, and
6 ones + 35 hundredths + 7 thousandths.

T: (Write 4 ones + 8 hundredths – 2 ones = _____ ones _____ hundredths.) Write the subtraction sentence in decimal form.
S: (Write 4.08 – 2 = 2.08.)

More practice!

9 tenths + 7 thousandths – 4 thousandths,
4 ones + 582 thousandths – 3 hundredths,
9 ones + 708 thousandths – 4 tenths, and
4 ones + 73 thousandths – 4 hundredths.

---

fluency activities

Lesson 28:   Solidify fluency with Grade 5 skills.

Decompose Decimals

Materials: (S) Personal white board

T: (Project 7.463.) Say the number.

S: 7 and 463 thousandths.

T: Represent this number in a two-part number bond with ones as one part and thousandths as the other part.

S: (Draw.)

T: Represent it again with tenths and thousandths.

S: (Draw.)

T: Represent it again with hundredths and thousandths.

More practice!

8.972 and 6.849.

Find the Volume

Materials: (S) Personal white board

T: On your personal white board, write the formula for finding the volume of a rectangular prism.

S: (Write V = l × w × h.)

T: (Draw and label a rectangular prism with a length of 5 cm, width of 6 cm, and height of 2 cm.) Write a multiplication sentence to find the volume of this rectangular prism.

S: (Beneath V = l × w × h, write V = 5 cm × 6 cm × 2 cm. Beneath it, write V = 60 cm^3.)

More practice!

l = 7 ft, w = 9 ft, h = 3 ft;

l = 6 in, w = 6 in, h = 5 in; and

l = 4 cm, w = 8 cm, h = 2 cm.

Make a Like Unit

Materials: (S) Personal white board

T: I'll say two unit fractions. You make the like unit, and write it on your personal white board. Show your board at the signal.

T: $\frac{1}{3}$ and $\frac{1}{2}$. (Pause. Signal.)

S: (Write and show sixths.)

More practice!

$\frac{1}{4}$ and $\frac{1}{3}$, $\frac{1}{2}$ and $\frac{1}{4}$, $\frac{1}{6}$ and $\frac{1}{2}$, $\frac{1}{3}$ and $\frac{1}{12}$, $\frac{1}{6}$ and $\frac{1}{8}$, and $\frac{1}{3}$ and $\frac{1}{9}$.

Unit Conversions

Materials: (S) Personal white board

T: (Write 12 in = _____ ft.) On your personal white board, write 12 inches is the same as how many feet?

S: (Write 1 foot.)

More practice!

24 in, 36 in, 54 in, and 76 in.

T: (Write 1 ft = _____ in.) Write 1 foot is the same as how many inches?

S: (Write 12 inches.)

More practice!

2 ft, 2.5 ft, 3 ft, 3.5 ft, 4 ft, 4.5 ft, 9 ft, and 9.5 ft.

fluency activities

Lesson 28:   Solidify fluency with Grade 5 skills.

Compare Decimal Fractions

Materials: (S) Personal white board

T: (Write 13.78 ___ 13.86.) On your personal white board, compare the numbers using the greater than, less than, or equal sign.

S: (Write 13.78 < 13.86.)

More practice!

0.78 ___ $\frac{78}{100}$, 439.3 ___ 4.39, 5.08 ___ fifty-eight tenths, and thirty-five and 9 thousandths ___ 4 tens.

Round to the Nearest One

Materials: (S) Personal white board

T: (Write 3 ones 2 tenths.) Write 3 ones and 2 tenths as a decimal.

S: (Write 3.2.)

T: (Write 3.2 ≈ ___.) Round 3 and 2 tenths to the nearest whole number.

S: (Write 3.2 ≈ 3.)

More practice!

3.7, 13.7, 5.4, 25.4, 1.5, 21.5, 6.48, 3.62, and 36.52.

Multiplying Fractions

Materials: (S) Personal white board

T: (Write $\frac{1}{2} \times \frac{1}{3}$ = ___.) Write the complete multiplication sentence.

S: (Write $\frac{1}{2} \times \frac{1}{3} = \frac{1}{6}$.)

T: (Write $\frac{1}{2} \times \frac{3}{4}$ = ___.) Write the complete multiplication sentence.

S: (Write $\frac{1}{2} \times \frac{3}{4} = \frac{3}{8}$.)

T: (Write $\frac{2}{5} \times \frac{2}{3}$ = ___.) Write the complete multiplication sentence.

S: (Write $\frac{2}{5} \times \frac{2}{3} = \frac{4}{15}$.)

More practice!

$\frac{1}{2} \times \frac{1}{5}, \frac{1}{2} \times \frac{3}{5}, \frac{3}{4} \times \frac{3}{5}, \frac{4}{5} \times \frac{2}{3}$, and $\frac{3}{4} \times \frac{5}{6}$.

Divide Whole Numbers by Unit Fractions

Materials: (S) Personal white board

T: (Write $1 \div \frac{1}{2}$.) How many halves are in 1?

S: 2.

T: (Write $1 \div \frac{1}{2} = 2$. Beneath it, write $2 \div \frac{1}{2}$.) How many halves are in 2?

S: 4.

T: (Write $2 \div \frac{1}{2} = 4$. Beneath it, write $3 \div \frac{1}{2}$.) How many halves are in 3?

S: 6.

T: (Write $3 \div \frac{1}{2} = 6$. Beneath it, write $7 \div \frac{1}{2}$.) Write the complete division sentence.

S: (Write $7 \div \frac{1}{2} = 14$.)

More practice!

$1 \div \frac{1}{3}, 2 \div \frac{1}{5}, 9 \div \frac{1}{4}$, and $3 \div \frac{1}{8}$.

---

fluency activities

A quadrilateral with two pairs of equal sides that are also adjacent.	An angle that turns through $\frac{1}{360}$ of a circle.	A quadrilateral with at least one pair of parallel lines.	A closed figure made up of line segments.
Measurement of space or capacity.	A quadrilateral with opposite sides that are parallel.	An angle measuring 90 degrees.	The union of two different rays sharing a common vertex.
The number of square units that cover a two-dimensional shape.	Two lines in a plane that do not intersect.	The number of adjacent layers of the base that form a rectangular prism.	A three-dimensional figure with six square sides.
A quadrilateral with four 90-degree angles.	A polygon with 4 sides and 4 angles.	A parallelogram with all equal sides.	Cubes of the same size used for measuring.
Two intersecting lines that form 90-degree angles.	A three-dimensional figure with six rectangular sides.	A three-dimensional figure.	Any flat surface of a 3-D figure.
A line that cuts a line segment into two equal parts at 90 degrees.	Squares of the same size, used for measuring.	A rectangular prism with only 90-degree angles.	One face of a 3-D solid, often thought of as the surface upon which the solid rests.

Lesson 29: Solidify the vocabulary of geometry.

Base	Volume of a Solid	Cubic Units	Kite
Height	One-Degree Angle	Face	Trapezoid
Right Rectangular Prism	Perpendicular Bisector	Cube	Area
Perpendicular Lines	Rhombus	Parallel Lines	Angle
Polygon	Rectangular Prism	Parallelogram	Rectangle
Right Angle	Quadrilateral	Solid Figure	Square Units

Lesson 29:   Solidify the vocabulary of geometry.

Name _____ Date _____

1. Use your ruler, protractor, and set square to help you give as many names as possible for each figure below. Then, explain your reasoning for how you named each figure.

Figure	Names	Reasoning for Names
a. 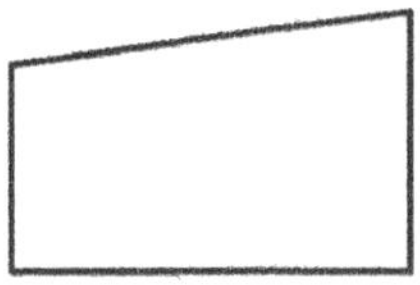		
b. 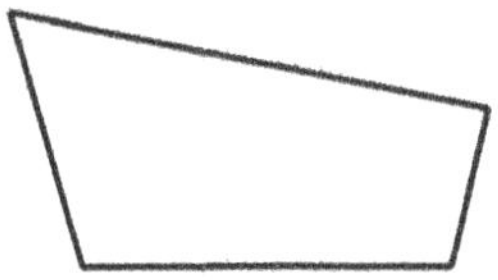		
c.		
d. 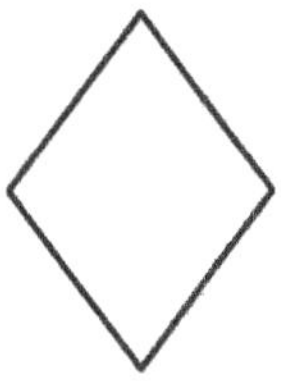		

2. Mark draws a figure that has the following characteristics:

   ▪ Exactly 4 sides that are each 7 centimeters long

   ▪ Two sets of parallel lines

   ▪ Exactly 4 angles that measure 35 degrees, 145 degrees, 35 degrees, and 145 degrees

   a. Draw and label Mark's figure below.

   b. Give as many names of quadrilaterals as possible for Mark's figure. Explain your reasoning for the names of Mark's figure.

   c. List the names of Mark's figure in Problem 2(b) in order from least specific to most specific. Explain your thinking.

Math Pictionary:

Number of players: 4–8

Materials: Blank paper, timer, pencils

- Players divide into two teams. The vocabulary term cards are placed facedown in a pile.

- A player from Team A chooses a card, silently reads the card, and draws a picture to represent the term on the card.

- As soon as the player silently reads the card, Team B starts the 30-second timer.

- Team A players use the drawing to figure out the term before the timer sounds.

- If the members of Team A correctly guess the term, they score a point for their team.

- However, the *first* wrong guess from Team A passes play to Team B. Team B then draws a picture to steal the point from Team A.

- Play continues with teams taking turns drawing until all cards have been used. The team with the most points wins.

Math Pictionary:

Number of players: 4–8

Materials: Blank paper, timer, pencils

- Players divide into two teams. The vocabulary term cards are placed facedown in a pile.

- A player from Team A chooses a card, silently reads the card, and draws a picture to represent the term on the card.

- As soon as the player silently reads the card, Team B starts the 30-second timer.

- Team A players use the drawing to figure out the term before the timer sounds.

- If the members of Team A correctly guess the term, they score a point for their team.

- However, the *first* wrong guess from Team A passes play to Team B. Team B then draws a picture to steal the point from Team A.

- Play continues with teams taking turns drawing until all cards have been used. The team with the most points wins.

math Pictionary directions

Attribute Buzz:

Number of players: 2

Description: Players place geometry vocabulary cards facedown in a pile and, as they select cards, name the attributes of each figure within 1 minute.

- Player A flips the first card and says as many attributes as possible within 30 seconds.
- Player B says, "Buzz," when or if Player A states an incorrect attribute or time is up.
- Player B explains why the attribute is incorrect (if applicable) and can then start listing attributes about the figure for 30 seconds.
- Players score a point for each correct attribute.
- Play continues until students have exhausted the figure's attributes. A new card is selected, and play continues. The player with the most points at the end of the game wins.

Concentration:

Number of players: 2–6

Description: Players persevere to match term cards with their definition and description cards.

- Create two identical arrays side by side: one of term cards and one of definition and description cards.
- Players take turns flipping over pairs of cards to find a match. A match is a vocabulary term and its definition or description card. Cards keep their precise location in the array if not matched. Remaining cards are not reconfigured into a new array.
- After all cards are matched, the player with the most pairs is the winner.

Three Questions to Guess My Term!

Number of players: 2–4

Description: A player selects and secretly views a term card. Other players take turns asking yes or no questions about the term.

- Players can keep track of what they know about the term on paper.
- Only yes or no questions are allowed. ("What kind of angles do you have?" is not allowed.)
- A final guess must be made after 3 questions but may be made sooner. Once a player says, "This is my guess," no more questions may be asked by that player.
- If the term is guessed correctly after 1 or 2 questions, 2 points are earned. If all 3 questions are used, only 1 point is earned.
- If no player guesses correctly, the card holder receives the point.
- The game continues as the player to the card holder's left selects a new card and questioning begins again.
- The game ends when a player reaches a predetermined score.

Bingo:

Number of players: 4–whole class

Description: Players match definitions to terms to be the first to fill a row, column, or diagonal.

- Players write a vocabulary term in each box of the math bingo game template. Each term should be used only once. The box that says "Math Bingo" is a free space.
- Players place the filled-in math bingo template in their personal white boards.
- One person is the caller and reads the definition on a vocabulary card.
- Players cross off or cover the term that matches the definition.
- "Bingo!" is called when 5 vocabulary terms in a row are crossed off diagonally, vertically, or horizontally. The free space counts as 1 box toward the needed 5 vocabulary terms.
- The first player to have 5 in a row reads each crossed-off word, states the definition, and gives a description or an example of each word. If all words are reasonably explained as determined by the caller, the player is declared the winner.

Name _____   Date _____

Teach someone at home how to play one of the games you played today with your pictorial vocabulary cards. Then, answer the questions below.

1. What games did you play?

2. Who played the games with you?

3. What was it like to teach someone at home how to play?

4. Did you have to teach the person who played with you any of the math concepts before you could play? Which ones? What was that like?

5. When you play these games at home again, what changes will you make? Why?

		Math BINGO!		

		Math BINGO!		

bingo card

Lesson 30:   Solidify the vocabulary of geometry.

163

Name _____   Date _____

Name _____ Date _____

1. List the Fibonacci numbers up to 21, and create, on the graph below, a spiral of squares corresponding to each of the numbers you write.

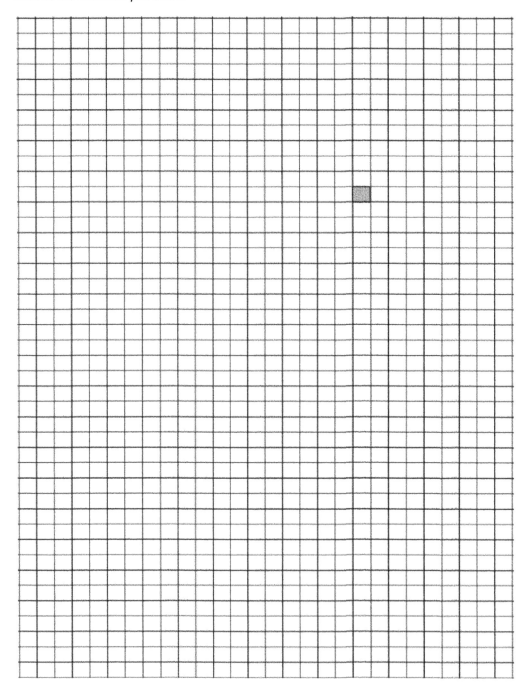

2. In the space below, write a rule that generates the Fibonacci sequence.

3. Write at least the first 15 numbers of the Fibonacci sequence.

Name _____   Date _____

1. Ashley decides to save money this year, but she wants to build it up over the year. She decides to start with $1.00 and add 1 more dollar each week of the year. Complete the table to show how much she will have saved by the end of the year.

Week	Add	Total	Week	Add	Total
1	$1.00	$1.00	27		
2	$2.00	$3.00	28		
3	$3.00	$6.00	29		
4	$4.00	$10.00	30		
5			31		
6			32		
7			33		
8			34		
9			35		
10			36		
11			37		
12			38		
13			39		
14			40		
15			41		
16			42		
17			43		
18			44		
19			45		
20			46		
21			47		
22			48		
23			49		
24			50		
25			51		
26			52		

EUREKA
MATH™

Lesson 32:   Explore patterns in saving money.

2. Carly wants to save money, too, but she has to start with the smaller denomination of quarters. Complete the second chart to show how much she will have saved by the end of the year if she adds a quarter more each week. Try it yourself, if you can and want to!

Week	Add	Total	Week	Add	Total
1	$0.25	$0.25	27		
2	$0.50	$0.75	28		
3	$0.75	$1.50	29		
4	$1.00	$2.50	30		
5			31		
6			32		
7			33		
8			34		
9			35		
10			36		
11			37		
12			38		
13			39		
14			40		
15			41		
16			42		
17			43		
18			44		
19			45		
20			46		
21			47		
22			48		
23			49		
24			50		
25			51		
26			52		

3. David decides he wants to save even more money than Ashley did. He does so by adding the next Fibonacci number instead of adding $1.00 each week. Use your calculator to fill in the chart and find out how much money he will have saved by the end of the year. Is this realistic for most people? Explain your answer.

Week	Add	Total		Week	Add	Total
1	$1	$1		27		
2	$1	$2		28		
3	$2	$4		29		
4	$3	$7		30		
5	$5	$12		31		
6	$8	$20		32		
7				33		
8				34		
9				35		
10				36		
11				37		
12				38		
13				39		
14				40		
15				41		
16				42		
17				43		
18				44		
19				45		
20				46		
21				47		
22				48		
23				49		
24				50		
25				51		
26				52		

Name _____   Date _____

1. Jonas played with the Fibonacci sequence he learned in class. Complete the table he started.

1	2	3	4	5	6	7	8	9	10
1	1	2	3	5	8				

11	12	13	14	15	16	17	18	19	20

2. As he looked at the numbers, Jonas realized he could play with them. He took two consecutive numbers in the pattern and multiplied them by themselves and then added them together. He found they made another number in the pattern. For example, $(3 \times 3) + (2 \times 2) = 13$, another number in the pattern. Jonas said this was true for any two consecutive Fibonacci numbers. Was Jonas correct? Show your reasoning by giving at least two examples of why he was or was not correct.

3. Fibonacci numbers can be found in many places in nature. For example, the number of petals in a daisy, the number of spirals in a pine cone or a pineapple, and even the way branches grow on a tree. Find an example of something natural where you can see a Fibonacci number in action, and sketch it here.

Name _____ Date _____

Record the dimensions of your boxes and lid below. Explain your reasoning for the dimensions you chose for Box 2 and the lid.

BOX 1 (Can hold Box 2 inside.)

The dimensions of Box 1 are _____ × _____ × _____ .

Its volume is _____ .

BOX 2 (Fits inside of Box 1.)

The dimensions of Box 2 are _____ × _____ × _____ .

Reasoning:

LID (Fits snugly over Box 1 to protect the contents.)

The dimensions of the lid are _____ × _____ × _____ .

Reasoning:

Lesson 33:   Design and construct boxes to house materials for summer use.

1. What steps did you take to determine the dimensions of the lid?

2. Find the volume of Box 2. Then, find the difference in the volumes of Boxes 1 and 2.

3. Imagine Box 3 is created such that each dimension is 1 cm less than that of Box 2. What would the volume of Box 3 be?

    Lesson 33:   Design and construct boxes to house materials for summer use.

174

Name _____   Date _____

1. Find various rectangular boxes at your home. Use a ruler to measure the dimensions of each box to the nearest centimeter. Then, calculate the volume of each box. The first one is partially done for you.

Item	Length	Width	Height	Volume
Juice Box	11 cm	2 cm	5 cm	

2. The dimensions of a small juice box are 11 cm by 4 cm by 7 cm. The super-size juice box has the same height of 11 cm but double the volume. Give two sets of the possible dimensions of the super-size juice box and the volume.

EUREKA MATH™ | **Lesson 33:**   Design and construct boxes to house materials for summer use.

175

Name _____   Date _____

I reviewed _____'s work.

Use the chart below to evaluate your friend's two boxes and lid. Measure and record the dimensions, and calculate the box volumes. Then, assess suitability, and suggest improvements in the adjacent columns.

Dimensions and Volume	Is the box or lid suitable? Explain.	Suggestions for Improvement
BOX 1 dimensions: Total volume:		
BOX 2 dimensions: Total volume:		
LID dimensions:		

Lesson 34: Design and construct boxes to house materials for summer use.

177